Algebra 1

Study Guide and Intervention Workbook

New York, New York
Columbus, Ohio
Chicago, Illinois
Peoria, Illinois
Woodland Hills, California

To The Student:

This *Study Guide and Intervention Workbook* gives you additional examples and problems for the concept exercises in each lesson. The exercises are designed to aid your study of algebra by reinforcing important mathematical skills needed to succeed in the everyday world. The material is organized by chapter and lesson, with two study guide worksheets for every lesson in *Glencoe Algebra 1*.

Always keep your workbook handy. Along with your textbook, daily homework, and class notes, the completed *Study Guide and Intervention Workbook* can help you in reviewing for quizzes and tests.

To the Teacher:

Answers to each worksheet are found in *Glencoe Chapter Resource Masters* and also in the Teacher Wraparound Edition of *Glencoe Algebra 1*.

Glencoe/McGraw-Hill

A Division of The McGraw·Hill Companies

Send all inquiries to:
The McGraw-Hill Companies
8787 Orion Place
Columbus, OH 43240

ISBN: 0-07-827753-1

Algebra 1
Study Guide and Intervention Workbook

14 15 16 009 10 09 08 07 06

Contents

1-1 Study Guide and Intervention

Variables and Expressions

Write Mathematical Expressions In the **algebraic expression**, ℓw, the letters ℓ and w are called **variables**. In algebra, a variable is used to represent unspecified numbers or values. Any letter can be used as a variable. The letters ℓ and w are used above because they are the first letters of the words *length* and *width*. In the expression ℓw, ℓ and w are called factors, and the result is called the **product**.

Example 1 Write an algebraic expression for each verbal expression.

a. four more than a number n

The words *more than* imply addition.
four more than a number n
$4 + n$
The algebraic expression is $4 + n$.

b. the difference of a number squared and 8

The expression *difference of* implies subtraction.
the difference of a number squared and 8
$n^2 - 8$
The algebraic expression is $n^2 - 8$.

Example 2 Evaluate each expression.

a. 3^4

$3^4 = 3 \cdot 3 \cdot 3 \cdot 3$ Use 3 as a factor 4 times.
$\quad = 81$ Multiply.

b. five cubed

Cubed means raised to the third power.
$5^3 = 5 \cdot 5 \cdot 5$ Use 5 as a factor 3 times.
$\quad = 125$ Multiply.

Exercises

Write an algebraic expression for each verbal expression.

1. a number decreased by 8

2. a number divided by 8

3. a number squared

4. four times a number

5. a number divided by 6

6. a number multiplied by 37

7. the sum of 9 and a number

8. 3 less than 5 times a number

9. twice the sum of 15 and a number

10. one-half the square of b

11. 7 more than the product of 6 and a number

12. 30 increased by 3 times the square of a number

Evaluate each expression.

13. 5^2

14. 3^3

15. 10^4

16. 12^2

17. 8^3

18. 2^8

1-1 Study Guide and Intervention *(continued)*

Variables and Expressions

Write Verbal Expressions Translating algebraic expressions into verbal expressions is important in algebra.

Example Write a verbal expression for each algebraic expression.

a. $6n^2$

the product of 6 and n squared

b. $n^3 - 12m$

the difference of n cubed and twelve times m

Exercises

Write a verbal expression for each algebraic expression.

1. $w - 1$

2. $\frac{1}{3}a^3$

3. $81 + 2x$

4. $12c$

5. 8^4

6. 6^2

7. $2n^2 + 4$

8. $a^3 \cdot b^3$

9. $2x^3 - 3$

10. $\frac{6k^3}{5}$

11. $\frac{1}{4}b^2$

12. $7n^5$

13. $3x + 4$

14. $\frac{2}{3}k^5$

15. $3b^2 + 2a^3$

16. $4(n^2 + 1)$

17. $3^2 + 2^3$

18. $6n^2 + 3$

1-2 Study Guide and Intervention

Order of Operations

Evaluate Rational Expressions Numerical expressions often contain more than one operation. To evaluate them, use the rules for order of operations shown below.

Order of Operations	**Step 1** Evaluate expressions inside grouping symbols.
	Step 2 Evaluate all powers.
	Step 3 Do all multiplication and/or division from left to right.
	Step 4 Do all addition and/or subtraction from left to right.

Example 1 Evaluate each expression.

a. $7 + 2 \cdot 4 - 4$

$$
\begin{aligned}
7 + 2 \cdot 4 - 4 &= 7 + 8 - 4 && \text{Multiply 2 and 4.} \\
&= 15 - 4 && \text{Add 7 and 8.} \\
&= 11 && \text{Subtract 4 from 15.}
\end{aligned}
$$

b. $3(2) + 4(2 + 6)$

$$
\begin{aligned}
3(2) + 4(2 + 6) &= 3(2) + 4(8) && \text{Add 2 and 6.} \\
&= 6 + 32 && \text{Multiply left to right.} \\
&= 38 && \text{Add 6 and 32.}
\end{aligned}
$$

Example 2 Evaluate each expression.

a. $3[2 + (12 \div 3)^2]$

$$
\begin{aligned}
3[2 + (12 \div 3)^2] &= 3(2 + 4^2) && \text{Divide 12 by 3.} \\
&= 3(2 + 16) && \text{Find 4 squared.} \\
&= 3(18) && \text{Add 2 and 16.} \\
&= 54 && \text{Multiply 3 and 18.}
\end{aligned}
$$

b. $\dfrac{3 + 2^3}{4^2 \cdot 3}$

$$
\begin{aligned}
\frac{3 + 2^3}{4^2 \cdot 3} &= \frac{3 + 8}{4^2 \cdot 3} && \text{Evaluate power in numerator.} \\
&= \frac{11}{4^2 \cdot 3} && \text{Add 3 and 8 in the numerator.} \\
&= \frac{11}{16 \cdot 3} && \text{Evaluate power in denominator.} \\
&= \frac{11}{48} && \text{Multiply.}
\end{aligned}
$$

Exercises

Evaluate each expression.

1. $(8 - 4) \cdot 2$

2. $(12 + 4) \cdot 6$

3. $10 + 2 \cdot 3$

4. $10 + 8 \cdot 1$

5. $15 - 12 \div 4$

6. $\dfrac{15 + 60}{30 - 5}$

7. $12(20 - 17) - 3 \cdot 6$

8. $24 \div 3 \cdot 2 - 3^2$

9. $8^2 \div (2 \cdot 8) + 2$

10. $3^2 \div 3 + 2^2 \cdot 7 - 20 \div 5$

11. $\dfrac{4 + 3^2}{12 + 1}$

12. $\dfrac{8(2) - 4}{8 \div 4}$

13. $250 \div [5(3 \cdot 7 + 4)]$

14. $\dfrac{2 \cdot 4^2 - 8 \div 2}{(5 + 2) \cdot 2}$

15. $\dfrac{4 \cdot 3^2 - 3 \cdot 2}{3 \cdot 5}$

16. $\dfrac{4(5^2) - 4 \cdot 3}{4(4 \cdot 5 + 2)}$

17. $\dfrac{5^2 - 3}{20(3) + 2(3)}$

18. $\dfrac{8^2 - 2^2}{(2 \cdot 8) + 4}$

Lesson 1-2

1-2 **Study Guide and Intervention** *(continued)*

Order of Operations

Evaluate Algebraic Expressions Algebraic expressions may contain more than one operation. Algebraic expressions can be evaluated if the values of the variables are known. First, replace the variables by their values. Then use the order of operations to calculate the value of the resulting numerical expression.

Example **Evaluate $x^3 + 5(y - 3)$ if $x = 2$ and $y = 12$.**

$$
\begin{aligned}
x^3 + 5(y - 3) &= 2^3 + 5(12 - 3) &&\text{Replace } x \text{ with 2 and } y \text{ with 12.} \\
&= 8 + 5(12 - 3) &&\text{Evaluate } 2^3. \\
&= 8 + 5(9) &&\text{Subtract 3 from 12.} \\
&= 8 + 45 &&\text{Multiply 5 and 9.} \\
&= 53 &&\text{Add 8 and 45.}
\end{aligned}
$$

The solution is 53.

Exercises

Evaluate each expression if $x = 2$, $y = 3$, $z = 4$, $a = \dfrac{4}{5}$, and $b = \dfrac{3}{5}$.

1. $x + 7$ **2.** $3x - 5$ **3.** $x + y^2$

4. $x^3 + y + z^2$ **5.** $6a + 8b$ **6.** $23 - (a + b)$

7. $\dfrac{y^2}{x^2}$ **8.** $2xyz + 5$ **9.** $x(2y + 3z)$

10. $(10x)^2 + 100a$ **11.** $\dfrac{3xy - 4}{7x}$ **12.** $a^2 + 2b$

13. $\dfrac{z^2 - y^2}{x^2}$ **14.** $6xz + 5xy$ **15.** $\dfrac{(z - y)^2}{x}$

16. $\dfrac{25ab + y}{xz}$ **17.** $\dfrac{5a^2b}{y}$ **18.** $(z \div x)^2 + ax$

19. $\left(\dfrac{x}{z}\right)^2 + \left(\dfrac{y}{z}\right)^2$ **20.** $\dfrac{x + z}{y + 2z}$ **21.** $\left(\dfrac{z \div x}{y}\right) + \left(\dfrac{y \div x}{z}\right)$

1-3 Study Guide and Intervention

Open Sentences

Solve Equations A mathematical sentence with one or more variables is called an **open sentence**. Open sentences are **solved** by finding replacements for the variables that result in true sentences. The set of numbers from which replacements for a variable may be chosen is called the **replacement set**. The set of all replacements for the variable that result in true statements is called the **solution set** for the variable. A sentence that contains an equal sign, =, is called an **equation**.

Example 1 Find the solution set of $3a + 12 = 39$ if the replacement set is {6, 7, 8, 9, 10}.

Replace a in $3a + 12 = 39$ with each value in the replacement set.

$3(6)+ 12 \stackrel{?}{=} 39 \rightarrow 30 \neq 39$ false
$3(7)+ 12 \stackrel{?}{=} 39 \rightarrow 33 \neq 39$ false
$3(8)+ 12 \stackrel{?}{=} 39 \rightarrow 36 \neq 39$ false
$3(9)+ 12 \stackrel{?}{=} 39 \rightarrow 39 = 39$ true
$3(10)+ 12 \stackrel{?}{=} 39 \rightarrow 42 \neq 39$ false

Since $a = 9$ makes the equation $3a + 12 = 39$ true, the solution is 9. The solution set is {9}.

Example 2 Solve $\dfrac{2(3 + 1)}{3(7 - 4)} = b$.

$\dfrac{2(3 + 1)}{3(7 - 4)} = b$ Original equation

$\dfrac{2(4)}{3(3)} = b$ Add in the numerator; subtract in the denominator.

$\dfrac{8}{9} = b$ Simplify.

The solution is $\dfrac{8}{9}$.

Exercises

Find the solution of each equation if the replacement sets are $X = \left\{\dfrac{1}{4}, \dfrac{1}{2}, 1, 2, 3\right\}$ and $Y = \{2, 4, 6, 8\}$.

1. $x + \dfrac{1}{2} = \dfrac{5}{2}$

2. $x + 8 = 11$

3. $y - 2 = 6$

4. $x^2 - 1 = 8$

5. $y^2 - 2 = 34$

6. $x^2 + 5 = 5\dfrac{1}{16}$

7. $2(x + 3) = 7$

8. $\dfrac{1}{4}(y + 1)^2 = \dfrac{9}{4}$

9. $y^2 + y = 20$

Solve each equation.

10. $a = 2^3 - 1$

11. $n = 6^2 - 4^2$

12. $w = 6^2 \cdot 3^2$

13. $\dfrac{1}{4} + \dfrac{5}{8} = k$

14. $\dfrac{18 - 3}{2 + 3} = p$

15. $s = \dfrac{15 - 6}{27 - 24}$

16. $18.4 - 3.2 = m$

17. $k = 9.8 + 5.7$

18. $c = 3\dfrac{1}{2} + 2\dfrac{1}{4}$

Lesson 1-3

1-3 Study Guide and Intervention (continued)

Open Sentences

Solve Inequalities An open sentence that contains the symbol $<$, $\leq$, $>$, or $\geq$ is called an **inequality**. Inequalities can be solved the same way that equations are solved.

Example **Find the solution set for $3a - 8 > 10$ if the replacement set is {4, 5, 6, 7, 8}.**

Replace a in $3a - 8 > 10$ with each value in the replacement set.

$3(4) - 8 \overset{?}{>} 10 \rightarrow 4 > 10$ false
$3(5) - 8 \overset{?}{>} 10 \rightarrow 7 > 10$ false
$3(6) - 8 \overset{?}{>} 10 \rightarrow 10 > 10$ false
$3(7) - 8 \overset{?}{>} 10 \rightarrow 13 > 10$ true
$3(8) - 8 \overset{?}{>} 10 \rightarrow 16 > 10$ true

Since replacing a with 7 or 8 makes the inequality $3a - 8 > 10$ true, the solution set is {7, 8}.

Exercises

Find the solution set for each inequality if the replacement set is
$X = \{0, 1, 2, 3, 4, 5, 6, 7\}$.

1. $x + 2 > 4$

2. $x \div 3 < 6$

3. $3x > 18$

4. $\dfrac{x}{3} > 1$

5. $\dfrac{x}{5} \geq 2$

6. $\dfrac{3x}{8} \leq 2$

7. $3x - 4 > 5$

8. $3(8 - x) + 1 \leq 6$

9. $4(x + 3) \geq 20$

Find the solution set for each inequality if the replacement sets are
$X = \left\{\dfrac{1}{4}, \dfrac{1}{2}, 1, 2, 3, 5, 8\right\}$ and $Y = \{2, 4, 6, 8, 10\}$

10. $x + 3 > 5$

11. $y \div 3 < 6$

12. $8y + 3 \geq 51$

13. $\dfrac{x}{2} < 4$

14. $\dfrac{y}{4} \geq 2$

15. $\dfrac{2y}{5} \leq 2$

16. $4x + 1 \geq 4$

17. $3x + 3 \geq 12$

18. $2(y + 1) \geq 18$

19. $3x - \dfrac{1}{4} < 2$

20. $3y + 2 \leq 8$

21. $\dfrac{1}{2}(6 - 2x) + 2 \leq 3$

1-4 Study Guide and Intervention

Identity and Equality Properties

Identity and Equality Properties The identity and equality properties in the chart below can help you solve algebraic equations and evaluate mathematical expressions.

Additive Identity	For any number a, $a + 0 = a$.
Multiplicative Identity	For any number a, $a \cdot 1 = a$.
Multiplicative Property of 0	For any number a, $a \cdot 0 = 0$.
Multiplicative Inverse Property	For every number $\frac{a}{b}$, $a, b \neq 0$, there is exactly one number $\frac{b}{a}$ such that $\frac{a}{b} \cdot \frac{b}{a} = 1$.
Reflexive Property	For any number a, $a = a$.
Symmetric Property	For any numbers a and b, if $a = b$, then $b = a$.
Transitive Property	For any numbers a, b, and c, if $a = b$ and $b = c$, then $a = c$.
Substitution Property	If $a = b$, then a may be replaced by b in any expression.

Example 1 Name the property used in each equation. Then find the value of n.

a. $8n = 8$
  Multiplicative Identity Property
  $n = 1$, since $8 \cdot 1 = 8$

b. $n \cdot 3 = 1$
  Multiplicative Inverse Property
  $n = \frac{1}{3}$, since $\frac{1}{3} \cdot 3 = 1$

Example 2 Name the property used to justify each statement.

a $5 + 4 = 5 + 4$
  Reflexive Property

b. If $n = 12$, then $4n = 4 \cdot 12$.
  Substitution Property

Exercises

Name the property used in each equation. Then find the value of n.

1. $6n = 6$ **2.** $n \cdot 1 = 8$ **3.** $6 \cdot n = 6 \cdot 9$

4. $9 = n + 9$ **5.** $n + 0 = \frac{3}{8}$ **6.** $\frac{3}{4} \cdot n = 1$

Name the property used in each equation.

7. If $4 + 5 = 9$, then $9 = 4 + 5$. **8.** $0 + 21 = 21$

9. $0(15) = 0$ **10.** $(1)94 = 94$

11. If $3 + 3 = 6$ and $6 = 3 \cdot 2$, then $3 + 3 = 3 \cdot 2$.

12. $4 + 3 = 4 + 3$ **13.** $(14 - 6) + 3 = 8 + 3$

Lesson 1-4

1-4 Study Guide and Intervention (continued)

Identity and Equality Properties

Use Identity and Equality Properties The properties of identity and equality can be used to justify each step when evaluating an expression.

Example Evaluate $24 \cdot 1 - 8 + 5(9 \div 3 - 3)$. Name the property used in each step.

$$
\begin{aligned}
24 \cdot 1 - 8 + 5(9 \div 3 - 3) &= 24 \cdot 1 - 8 + 5(3 - 3) && \text{Substitution; } 9 \div 3 = 3 \\
&= 24 \cdot 1 - 8 + 5(0) && \text{Substitution; } 3 - 3 = 0 \\
&= 24 - 8 + 5(0) && \text{Multiplicative Identity; } 24 \cdot 1 = 24 \\
&= 24 - 8 + 0 && \text{Multiplicative Property of Zero; } 5(0) = 0 \\
&= 16 + 0 && \text{Substitution; } 24 - 8 = 16 \\
&= 16 && \text{Additive Identity; } 16 + 0 = 16
\end{aligned}
$$

Exercises

Evaluate each expression. Name the property used in each step.

1. $2\left[\dfrac{1}{4} + \left(\dfrac{1}{2}\right)^2\right]$

2. $15 \cdot 1 - 9 + 2(15 \div 3 - 5)$

3. $2(3 \cdot 5 \cdot 1 - 14) - 4 \cdot \dfrac{1}{4}$

4. $18 \cdot 1 - 3 \cdot 2 + 2(6 \div 3 - 2)$

5. $10 \div 5 - 2^2 \div 2 + 13$

6. $3(5 - 5 \cdot 1^2) + 21 \div 7$

1-5 Study Guide and Intervention

The Distributive Property

Evaluate Expressions The Distributive Property can be used to help evaluate expressions.

Distributive Property	For any numbers a, b, and c, $a(b + c) = ab + ac$ and $(b + c)a = ba + ca$ and $a(b - c) = ab - ac$ and $(b - c)a = ba - ca$.

Example 1 **Rewrite 6(8 + 10) using the Distributive Property. Then evaluate.**

$6(8 + 10) = 6 \cdot 8 + 6 \cdot 10$ Distributive Property
$ = 48 + 60$ Multiply.
$ = 108$ Add.

Example 2 **Rewrite $-2(3x^2 + 5x + 1)$ using the Distributive Property. Then simplify.**

$-2(3x^2 + 5x + 1) = -2(3x^2) + (-2)(5x) + (-2)(1)$ Distributive Property
$ = -6x^2 + (-10x) + (-2)$ Multiply.
$ = -6x^2 - 10x - 2$ Simplify.

Exercises

Rewrite each expression using the Distributive Property. Then simplify.

1. $2(10 - 5)$ **2.** $6(12 - t)$ **3.** $3(x - 1)$

4. $6(12 + 5)$ **5.** $(x - 4)3$ **6.** $-2(x + 3)$

7. $5(4x - 9)$ **8.** $3(8 - 2x)$ **9.** $12\left(6 - \frac{1}{2}x\right)$

10. $12\left(2 + \frac{1}{2}x\right)$ **11.** $\frac{1}{4}(12 - 4t)$ **12.** $3(2x - y)$

13. $2(3x + 2y - z)$ **14.** $(x - 2)y$ **15.** $2(3a - 2b + c)$

16. $\frac{1}{4}(16x - 12y + 4z)$ **17.** $(2 - 3x + x^2)3$ **18.** $-2(2x^2 + 3x + 1)$

Lesson 1-5

1-5 Study Guide and Intervention (continued)

The Distributive Property

Simplify Expressions A **term** is a number, a variable, or a product or quotient of numbers and variables. **Like terms** are terms that contain the same variables, with corresponding variables having the same powers. The Distributive Property and properties of equalities can be used to simplify expressions. An expression is in **simplest form** if it is replaced by an **equivalent** expression with no like terms or parentheses.

Example   Simplify $4(a^2 + 3ab) - ab$.

$$
\begin{aligned}
4(a^2 + 3ab) - ab &= 4(a^2 + 3ab) - 1ab && \text{Multiplicative Identity}\\
&= 4a^2 + 12ab - 1ab && \text{Distributive Property}\\
&= 4a^2 + (12 - 1)ab && \text{Distributive Property}\\
&= 4a^2 + 11ab && \text{Substitution}
\end{aligned}
$$

Exercises

Simplify each expression. If not possible, write *simplified*.

1. $12a - a$

2. $3x + 6x$

3. $3x - 1$

4. $12g - 10g + 1$

5. $-2x - 12$

6. $4x^2 + 3x + 7$

7. $20a + 12a - 8$

8. $3x^2 + 2x^2$

9. $-6x + 3x^2 + 10x^2$

10. $2p + \frac{1}{2}q$

11. $10xy - 4(xy + xy)$

12. $21c + 18c + 31b - 3b$

13. $3x - 2x - 2y + 2y$

14. $xy - 2xy$

15. $12a - 12b + 12c$

16. $4x + \frac{1}{4}(16x - 20y)$

17. $2 - 1 - 6x + x^2$

18. $4x^2 + 3x^2 + 2x$

1-6 Study Guide and Intervention

Commutative and Associative Properties

Commutative and Associative Properties The Commutative and Associative Properties can be used to simplify expressions. The Commutative Properties state that the order in which you add or multiply numbers does not change their sum or product. The Associative Properties state that the way you group three or more numbers when adding or multiplying does not change their sum or product.

Commutative Properties	For any numbers a and b, $a + b = b + a$ and $a \cdot b = b \cdot a$.
Associative Properties	For any numbers a, b, and c, $(a + b) + c = a + (b + c)$ and $(ab)c = a(bc)$.

Example 1 Evaluate $6 \cdot 2 \cdot 3 \cdot 5$.

$$
\begin{aligned}
6 \cdot 2 \cdot 3 \cdot 5 &= 6 \cdot 3 \cdot 2 \cdot 5 && \text{Commutative Property}\\
&= (6 \cdot 3)(2 \cdot 5) && \text{Associative Property}\\
&= 18 \cdot 10 && \text{Multiply.}\\
&= 180 && \text{Multiply.}
\end{aligned}
$$

The product is 180.

Example 2 Evaluate $8.2 + 2.5 + 2.5 + 1.8$.

$$
\begin{aligned}
8.2 + 2.5 + 2.5 + 1.8 & \\
&= 8.2 + 1.8 + 2.5 + 2.5 && \text{Commutative Prop.}\\
&= (8.2 + 1.8) + (2.5 + 2.5) && \text{Associative Prop.}\\
&= 10 + 5 && \text{Add.}\\
&= 15 && \text{Add.}
\end{aligned}
$$

The sum is 15.

Exercises

Evaluate each expression.

1. $12 + 10 + 8 + 5$

2. $16 + 8 + 22 + 12$

3. $10 \cdot 7 \cdot 2.5$

4. $4 \cdot 8 \cdot 5 \cdot 3$

5. $12 + 20 + 10 + 5$

6. $26 + 8 + 4 + 22$

7. $3\frac{1}{2} + 4 + 2\frac{1}{2} + 3$

8. $\frac{3}{4} \cdot 12 \cdot 4 \cdot 2$

9. $3.5 + 2.4 + 3.6 + 4.2$

10. $4\frac{1}{2} + 5 + \frac{1}{2} + 3$

11. $0.5 \cdot 2.8 \cdot 4$

12. $2.5 + 2.4 + 2.5 + 3.6$

13. $\frac{4}{5} \cdot 18 \cdot 25 \cdot \frac{2}{9}$

14. $32 \cdot \frac{1}{5} \cdot \frac{1}{2} \cdot 10$

15. $\frac{1}{4} \cdot 7 \cdot 16 \cdot \frac{1}{7}$

16. $3.5 + 8 + 2.5 + 2$

17. $18 \cdot 8 \cdot \frac{1}{2} \cdot \frac{1}{9}$

18. $\frac{3}{4} \cdot 10 \cdot 16 \cdot \frac{1}{2}$

1-6 Study Guide and Intervention (continued)

Commutative and Associative Properties

Simplify Expressions The Commutative and Associative Properties can be used along with other properties when evaluating and simplifying expressions.

Example   Simplify $8(y + 2x) + 7y$.

$$
\begin{aligned}
8(y + 2x) + 7y &= 8y + 16x + 7y && \text{Distributive Property} \\
&= 8y + 7y + 16x && \text{Commutative } (+) \\
&= (8 + 7)y + 16x && \text{Distributive Property} \\
&= 15y + 16x && \text{Substitution}
\end{aligned}
$$

The simplified expression is $15y + 16x$.

Exercises

Simplify each expression.

1. $4x + 3y + x$

2. $3a + 4b + a$

3. $8rs + 2rs^2 + 7rs$

4. $3a^2 + 4b + 10a^2$

5. $6(x + y) + 2(2x + y)$

6. $6n + 2(4n + 5)$

7. $6(a + b) + a + 3b$

8. $5(2x + 3y) + 6(y + x)$

9. $5(0.3x + 0.1y) + 0.2x$

10. $\frac{2}{3} + \frac{1}{2}(x + 10) + \frac{4}{3}$

11. $z^2 + 9x^2 + \frac{4}{3}z^2 + \frac{1}{3}x^2$

12. $6(2x + 4y) + 2(x + 9)$

Write an algebraic expression for each verbal expression. Then simplify.

13. twice the sum of y and z is increased by y

14. four times the product of x and y decreased by $2xy$

15. the product of five and the square of a, increased by the sum of eight, a^2, and 4

16. three times the sum of x and y increased by twice the sum of x and y

1-7 Study Guide and Intervention

Logical Reasoning

Conditional Statements A **conditional statement** is a statement of the form *If A, then B*. Statements in this form are called **if-then statements**. The part of the statement immediately following the word *if* is called the **hypothesis**. The part of the statement immediately following the word *then* is called the **conclusion**.

Example 1 Identify the hypothesis and conclusion of each statement.

a. If it is Wednesday, then Jerri has aerobics class.

Hypothesis: it is Wednesday
Conclusion: Jerri has aerobics class

b. If $2x - 4 < 10$, then $x < 7$.

Hypothesis: $2x - 4 < 10$
Conclusion: $x < 7$

Example 2 Identify the hypothesis and conclusion of each statement. Then write the statement in if-then form.

a. You and Marylynn can watch a movie on Thursday.

Hypothesis: it is Thursday
Conclusion: you and Marylynn can watch a movie
If it is Thursday, then you and Marylynn can watch a movie.

b. For a number a such that $3a + 2 = 11$, $a = 3$.

Hypothesis: $3a + 2 = 11$
Conclusion: $a = 3$
If $3a + 2 = 11$, then $a = 3$.

Exercises

Identify the hypothesis and conclusion of each statement.

1. If it is April, then it might rain.

2. If you are a sprinter, then you can run fast.

3. If $12 - 4x = 4$, then $x = 2$.

4. If it is Monday, then you are in school.

5. If the area of a square is 49, then the square has side length 7.

Identify the hypothesis and conclusion of each statement. Then write the statement in if-then form.

6. A quadrilateral with equal sides is a rhombus.

7. A number that is divisible by 8 is also divisible by 4.

8. Karlyn goes to the movies when she does not have homework.

1-7 **Study Guide and Intervention** *(continued)*

Logical Reasoning

Deductive Reasoning and Counterexamples **Deductive reasoning** is the process of using facts, rules, definitions, or properties to reach a valid conclusion. To show that a conditional statement is false, use a **counterexample**, one example for which the conditional statement is false. You need to find only one counterexample for the statement to be false.

Example 1 Determine a valid conclusion from the statement *If two numbers are even, then their sum is even* for the given conditions. If a valid conclusion does not follow, write *no valid conclusion* and explain why.

a. The two numbers are 4 and 8.

4 and 8 are even, and $4 + 8 = 12$. Conclusion: The sum of 4 and 8 is even.

b. The sum of two numbers is 20.

Consider 13 and 7. $13 + 7 = 20$
However, $12 + 8$, $19 + 1$, and $18 + 2$ all equal 20. There is no way to determine the two numbers. Therefore there is no valid conclusion.

Example 2 Provide a counterexample to this conditional statement. *If you use a calculator for a math problem, then you will get the answer correct.*

Counterexample: If the problem is $475 \div 5$ and you press $475 - 5$, you will not get the correct answer.

Exercises

Determine a valid conclusion that follows from the statement *If the last digit of a number is 0 or 5, then the number is divisible by 5* for the given conditions. If a valid conclusion does not follow, write *no valid conclusion* and explain why.

1. The number is 120.

2. The number is a multiple of 4.

3. The number is 101.

Find a counterexample for each statement.

4. If Susan is in school, then she is in math class.

5. If a number is a square, then it is divisible by 2.

6. If a quadrilateral has 4 right angles, then the quadrilateral is a square.

7. If you were born in New York, then you live in New York.

8. If three times a number is greater than 15, then the number must be greater than six.

9. If $3x - 2 \le 10$, then $x < 4$.

1-8 Study Guide and Intervention

Graphs and Functions

Interpret Graphs A **function** is a relationship between input and output values. In a function, there is exactly one output for each input. The input values are associated with the **independent variable**, and the output values are associated with the **dependent variable**. Functions can be graphed without using a scale to show the general shape of the graph that represents the function.

Example 1 The graph below represents the height of a football after it is kicked downfield. Identify the independent and the dependent variable. Then describe what is happening in the graph.

The independent variable is time, and the dependent variable is height. The football starts on the ground when it is kicked. It gains altitude until it reaches a maximum height, then it loses altitude until it falls to the ground.

Example 2 The graph below represents the price of stock over time. Identify the independent and dependent variable. Then describe what is happening in the graph.

The independent variable is time and the dependent variable is price. The price increases steadily, then it falls, then increases, then falls again.

Exercises

1. The graph represents the speed of a car as it travels to the grocery store. Identify the independent and dependent variable. Then describe what is happening in the graph.

2. The graph represents the balance of a savings account over time. Identify the independent and the dependent variable. Then describe what is happening in the graph.

3. The graph represents the height of a baseball after it is hit. Identify the independent and the dependent variable. Then describe what is happening in the graph.

Glencoe Algebra 1

Lesson 1-8

1-8 Study Guide and Intervention (continued)

Graphs and Functions

Draw Graphs You can represent the graph of a function using a **coordinate system**. Input and output values are represented on the graph using **ordered pairs** of the form (x, y). The x-value, called the x-**coordinate**, corresponds to the x-axis, and the y-value, or y-**coordinate** corresponds to the y-axis. Graphs can be used to represent many real-world situations.

Example A music store advertises that if you buy 3 CDs at the regular price of $16, then you will receive one CD of the same or lesser value free.

a. Make a table showing the cost of buying 1 to 5 CDs.

Number of CDs	1	2	3	4	5
Total Cost ($)	16	32	48	48	64

b. Write the data as a set of ordered pairs.

(1, 16), (2, 32), (3, 48), (4, 48), (5, 64)

c. Draw a graph that shows the relationship between the number of CDs and the total cost.

Exercises

1. The table below represents the length of a baby versus its age in months.

Age (months)	0	1	2	3	4
Length (inches)	20	21	23	23	24

a. Identify the independent and dependent variables.

b. Write a set of ordered pairs representing the data in the table.

c. Draw a graph showing the relationship between age and inches.

2. The table below represents the value of a car versus its age.

Age (years)	0	1	2	3	4
Value ($)	20,000	18,000	16,000	14,000	13,000

a. Identify the independent and dependent variables.

b. Write a set of ordered pairs representing the data in the table.

c. Draw a graph showing the relationship between age and value.

1-9 Study Guide and Intervention

Statistics: Analyzing Data by Using Tables and Graphs

Analyze Data Graphs or tables can be used to display data. A **bar graph** compares different categories of data, while a **circle graph** compares parts of a set of data as a percent of the whole set. A **line graph** is useful to show how a data set changes over time.

Example The circle graph at the right shows the number of international visitors to the United States in 2000, by country.

a. If there were a total of 50,891,000 visitors, how many were from Mexico?

$50,891,000 \times 20\% = 10,178,200$

b. If the percentage of visitors from each country remains the same each year, how many visitors from Canada would you expect in the year 2003 if the total is 59,000,000 visitors?

$59,000,000 \times 29\% = 17,110,000$

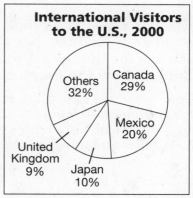

International Visitors to the U.S., 2000

Others 32%
Canada 29%
Mexico 20%
Japan 10%
United Kingdom 9%

Source: TInet

Exercises

1. The graph shows the use of imported steel by U. S. companies over a 10-year period.

  a. Describe the general trend in the graph.

  b. What would be a reasonable prediction for the percentage of imported steel used in 2002?

Imported Steel as Percent of Total Used

Source: *Chicago Tribune*

2. The table shows the percentage of change in worker productivity at the beginning of each year for a 5-year period.

  a. Which year shows the greatest percentage increase in productivity?

  b. What does the negative percent in the first quarter of 2001 indicate?

Worker Productivity Index	
Year (1st Qtr.)	% of Change
1997	+1
1998	+4.6
1999	+2
2000	+2.1
2001	−1.2

Source: *Chicago Tribune*

Lesson 1-9

1-9 Study Guide and Intervention (continued)

Statistics: Analyzing Data by Using Tables and Graphs

Misleading Graphs Graphs are very useful for displaying data. However, some graphs can be confusing, easily misunderstood, and lead to false assumptions. These graphs may be mislabeled or contain incorrect data. Or they may be constructed to make one set of data appear greater than another set.

Example **The graph at the right shows the number of students per computer in the U.S. public schools for the school years from 1995 to 1999. Explain how the graph misrepresents the data.**

The values are difficult to read because the vertical scale is too condensed. It would be more appropriate to let each unit on the vertical scale represent 1 student rather than 5 students and have the scale go from 0 to 12.

Source: *The World Almanac*

Exercises

Explain how each graph misrepresents the data.

1. The graph below shows the U.S. greenhouse gases emissions for 1999.

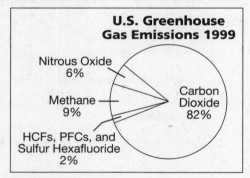

Source: Department of Energy

2. The graph below shows the amount of money spent on tourism for 1998-99.

Source: *The World Almanac*

2-1 Study Guide and Intervention

Rational Numbers on the Number Line

Graph Rational Numbers The figure at the right is part of a number line. A number line can be used to show the sets of **natural numbers**, **whole numbers**, and **integers**. **Positive numbers**, are located to the right of 0, and **negative numbers** are located to the left of 0.

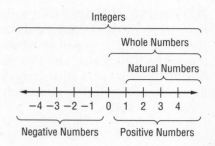

Another set of numbers that you can display on a number line is the set of **rational numbers**. A rational number can be written as $\frac{a}{b}$, where a and b are integers and $b \neq 0$. Some examples of rational numbers are $\frac{1}{4}$, $\frac{-3}{5}$, $\frac{-7}{-8}$, and $\frac{12}{-3}$.

Lesson 2-1

Example 1 Name the coordinates of the points graphed on each number line.

a.
$$-3 \ -2 \ -1 \ 0 \ 1 \ 2 \ 3 \ 4 \ 5$$

The dots indicate each point on the graph. The coordinates are $\{-3, -1, 1, 3, 5\}$

b.
$$1 \ 1.5 \ 2 \ 2.5 \ 3 \ 3.5 \ 4 \ 4.5 \ 5$$

The bold arrow to the right means the graph continues indefinitely in that direction. The coordinates are $\{2, 2.5, 3, 3.5, 4, 4.5, 5, \ldots\}$.

Example 2 Graph each set of numbers.

a. $\{\ldots, -3, -2, -1, 0, 1, 2\}$
$$-4 \ -3 \ -2 \ -1 \ 0 \ 1 \ 2 \ 3 \ 4$$

b. $\left\{-\frac{1}{3}, 0, \frac{1}{3}, \frac{2}{3}\right\}$
$$-\frac{2}{3} \ -\frac{1}{3} \ 0 \ \frac{1}{3} \ \frac{2}{3} \ 1 \ \frac{4}{3} \ \frac{5}{3} \ 2$$

Exercises

Name the coordinates of the points graphed on each number line.

1.
$$-2 \ -1 \ 0 \ 1 \ 2 \ 3 \ 4 \ 5 \ 6$$

2.
$$-1 \ 0 \ 1 \ 2 \ 3 \ 4 \ 5 \ 6 \ 7$$

3.
$$-\frac{1}{2} \ -\frac{1}{4} \ 0 \ \frac{1}{4} \ \frac{1}{2} \ \frac{3}{4} \ 1 \ \frac{5}{4} \ \frac{3}{2}$$

4.
$$-4 \ -3 \ -2 \ -1 \ 0 \ 1 \ 2 \ 3 \ 4$$

Graph each set of numbers.

5. $\{-3, -1, 1, 3\}$
$$-4 \ -3 \ -2 \ -1 \ 0 \ 1 \ 2 \ 3 \ 4$$

6. $\{-5, -2, 1, 2\}$
$$-5 \ -4 \ -3 \ -2 \ -1 \ 0 \ 1 \ 2 \ 3$$

7. {integers less than 0}
$$-4 \ -3 \ -2 \ -1 \ 0 \ 1 \ 2 \ 3 \ 4$$

8. $\{\ldots, -2, -1, 0, 1\}$

$$-4 \ -3 \ -2 \ -1 \ 0 \ 1 \ 2 \ 3 \ 4$$

9. $\left\{-2\frac{1}{2}, -1\frac{1}{2}, -\frac{1}{2}, \frac{1}{2}\right\}$
$$-3 \ -2\frac{1}{2} \ -2 \ -1\frac{1}{2} \ -1 \ -\frac{1}{2} \ 0 \ \frac{1}{2} \ 1$$

10. $\{\ldots, -4, -2, 0, 2, \ldots\}$

$$-6 \ -5 \ -4 \ -3 \ -2 \ -1 \ 0 \ 1 \ 2$$

2-1 Study Guide and Intervention (continued)

Rational Numbers on the Number Line

Absolute Value On a number line, −3 is three units from zero in the negative direction, and 3 is three units from zero in the positive direction. The number line at the right illustrates the meaning of **absolute value**. The absolute value of a number n is the distance from zero on a number line and is represented $|n|$. For this example, $|-3| = 3$ and $|3| = 3$.

Example 1 Find each absolute value.

a. $|-6|$

−6 is six units from zero in the negative direction.
$|-6| = 6$

b. $\left|\dfrac{3}{2}\right|$

$\dfrac{3}{2}$ is three halves units from zero in the positive direction.
$\left|\dfrac{3}{2}\right| = \dfrac{3}{2}$

Example 2 Evaluate $4 + |x - 2|$ if $x = 5$.

$$4 + |x - 2| = 4 + |5 - 2| \quad \text{Replace } x \text{ with 5.}$$
$$= 4 + |3| \quad 5 - 2 = 3$$
$$= 4 + 3 \quad |3| = 3$$
$$= 7 \quad \text{Simplify.}$$

Exercises

Find each absolute value.

1. $|2|$

2. $|-5|$

3. $|-24|$

4. $|-1.3|$

5. $\left|-\dfrac{2}{3}\right|$

6. $\left|\dfrac{35}{41}\right|$

Evaluate each expression if $a = 5$, $b = \dfrac{1}{4}$, $x = 8$, and $y = 2.5$.

7. $18 + |4 - y|$

8. $|x + 8| + 12$

9. $|x - 2| + 8.2$

10. $2 + |x - 5|$

11. $|2.5 + y| + 12$

12. $|23 - x| - 9$

13. $|x - 6| + 4.5$

14. $10 - |a - 2|$

15. $|6 + b| + \dfrac{1}{2}$

16. $\left|\dfrac{1}{4} + b\right| - \left|-\dfrac{1}{2}\right|$

17. $|3 + b| + a$

18. $|-b| + 1\dfrac{1}{2}$

2-2 Study Guide and Intervention

Adding and Subtracting Rational Numbers

Add Rational Numbers

Adding Rational Numbers, Same Sign	Add the numbers. If both are positive, the sum is positive; if both are negative, the sum is negative.
Adding Rational Numbers, Different Signs	Subtract the number with the lesser absolute value from the number with the greater absolute value. The sign of the sum is the same as the sign of the number with the greater absolute value.

Example 1 Use a number line to find the sum $-2 + (-3)$.

Step 1 Draw an arrow from 0 to -2.

Step 2 From the tip of the first arrow, draw a second arrow 3 units to the left to represent adding -3.

Step 3 The second arrow ends at the sum -5. So $-2 + (-3) = -5$.

Example 2 Find each sum.

a. $-8 + 5$

$$-8 + 5 = -(|-8| - |5|)$$
$$= -(8 - 5)$$
$$= -3$$

b. $\dfrac{3}{4} + \left(-\dfrac{1}{2}\right)$

$$\frac{3}{4} + \left(-\frac{1}{2}\right) = \frac{3}{4} + \left(-\frac{2}{4}\right)$$
$$= +\left(\left|\frac{3}{4}\right| - \left|-\frac{2}{4}\right|\right)$$
$$= +\left(\frac{3}{4} - \frac{2}{4}\right)$$
$$= \frac{1}{4}$$

Exercises

Find each sum.

1. $12 + 24$

2. $-6 + 14$

3. $-12 + (-15)$

4. $-21.5 + 34.2$

5. $8.2 + (-3.5)$

6. $23.5 + (-15.2)$

7. $90 + (-105)$

8. $108 + (-62)$

9. $-84 + (-90)$

10. $\dfrac{5}{7} + \dfrac{1}{3}$

11. $\dfrac{3}{14} + \dfrac{6}{17}$

12. $-\dfrac{4}{9} + \dfrac{3}{5}$

13. $-\dfrac{2}{3} + \left(-\dfrac{1}{4}\right)$

14. $-\dfrac{1}{5} + \dfrac{7}{11}$

15. $-\dfrac{18}{40} + \left(-\dfrac{10}{20}\right)$

16. $-\dfrac{3}{5} + \left(-\dfrac{5}{6}\right)$

17. $-1.6 + (-1.8)$

18. $-0.008 + (-0.25)$

Lesson 2-2

2-2 **Study Guide and Intervention** *(continued)*

Adding and Subtracting Rational Numbers

Subtract Rational Numbers Every positive rational number can be paired with a negative rational number so that their sum is 0. The numbers, called **opposites**, are **additive inverses** of each other.

Additive Inverse Property	For every number a, $a + (-a) = 0$.

To subtract a rational number, add its inverse and use the rules for addition given on page 81.

Subtraction of Rational Numbers	For any numbers a and b, $a - b = a + (-b)$.

Example Find $8.5 - 10.2$.

$$8.5 - 10.2 = 8.5 + (-10.2) \quad \text{To subtract 10.2, add its inverse.}$$
$$= -(|-10.2| - |8.5|) \quad |-10.2| \text{ is greater, so the result is negative.}$$
$$= -1.7 \quad \text{Simplify.}$$

Exercises

Find each difference.

1. $11 - 41$

2. $15 - (-21)$

3. $-33 - (-17)$

4. $18 - (-12)$

5. $15.5 - (-2.5)$

6. $65.8 - (-23.5)$

7. $90 - (-15)$

8. $-10.8 - (6.8)$

9. $-84 - (-72)$

10. $58.8 - (-11.2)$

11. $-18.2 - 3.2$

12. $-9 - (-5.6)$

13. $-\dfrac{1}{3} - \left(-\dfrac{3}{4}\right)$

14. $-\dfrac{1}{5} - \left(-\dfrac{4}{7}\right)$

15. $\dfrac{9}{4} - \dfrac{5}{9}$

16. $\dfrac{12}{23} - \left(-\dfrac{1}{2}\right)$

17. $-\dfrac{7}{8} - \left(-\dfrac{3}{9}\right)$

18. $\dfrac{24}{10} - \dfrac{18}{20}$

19. Sanelle was playing a video game. Her scores were $+50$, $+75$, -18, and -22. What was her final score?

20. The football team offense began a drive from their 20-yard line. They gained 8 yards, lost 12 yards and lost 2 yards before having to kick the ball. What yard line were they on when they had to kick the ball?

2-5 Study Guide and Intervention

Statistics: Displaying and Analyzing Data

Create Line Plots and Stem-and-Leaf Plots One way to display data graphically is with a **line plot**. A line plot is a number line labeled with a scale that includes all the data and $\times$s placed above a data point each time it occurs in the data list. The $\times$s represent the **frequency** of the data. A **stem-and-leaf plot** can also be used to organize data. The greatest *common* place value is called the stem, and the numbers in the next greatest place value form the leaves.

Example 1 Draw a line plot for the data.

$$-3 \quad 3 \quad 4 \quad 7 \quad 9 \quad 10 \quad -2 \quad 3$$
$$6 \quad 4 \quad 3 \quad 9 \quad -1 \quad -2 \quad 4 \quad 2$$

Step 1 The value of the data ranges from -3 to 10, so construct a number line containing those points.

Step 2 Then place an $\times$ above the number each time it occurs.

Example 2 Use the data below to create a stem-and-leaf plot.

$$62 \quad 74 \quad 89 \quad 102 \quad 92 \quad 65 \quad 68 \quad 98 \quad 78 \quad 65$$
$$78 \quad 80 \quad 83 \quad 93 \quad 87 \quad 89 \quad 104 \quad 109 \quad 104$$
$$68 \quad 97 \quad 68 \quad 64 \quad 98 \quad 93 \quad 90 \quad 102 \quad 104$$

The greatest common place value is tens, so the digits in the tens place are the stems. Thus 62 would have a stem of 6 and 104 would have a stem of ten. The stem-and-leaf plot is shown below.

Stem	Leaf
6	2 4 5 5 8 8 8
7	4 8 8
8	0 3 7 9 9
9	0 2 3 3 7 8 8
10	2 2 4 4 4 9

$6|2 = 62$

Exercises

Use the table at the right for Exercises 1–3.

1. Make a line plot representing the weights of the wrestlers shown in the table at the right.

Weights of Junior Varsity Wrestlers (pounds)							
170	160	135	135	160	122	188	154
108	135	140	122	103	190	154	

2. How many wrestlers weigh over 140 lb?

3. What is the greatest weight?

Use each set of data to make a stem-and-leaf plot.

4. 32 45 41 29 30 30 31 34 38
　　36 32 34 41 40 42 41 29 30

5. 102 104 99 109 108 112 115 120
　　112 114 98 94 96 101 100 102

Lesson 2-5

2-5 Study Guide and Intervention (continued)

Statistics: Displaying and Analyzing Data

Analyze Data Numbers that represent the centralized, or middle, value of a set of data are called **measures of central tendency**. Three measures of central tendency are the **mean**, **median**, and **mode**.

	Definition	Example
Mean	Sum of the data values divided by the number of values in the data set.	Data: 24, 36, 21, 30, 21, 30; $\dfrac{24 + 36 + 21 + 30 + 21 + 30}{6} = 27$
Median	The middle number in a data set when the numbers are arranged in numerical order. If there is an even number of values, the median is halfway between the two middle values.	Data: 21, 21, 25, 30, 31, 42; $\dfrac{25 + 30}{2} = 27.5$
Mode	The number or numbers that occur most often in the set of data.	Data: 21, 21, 24, 30, 30, 36; 21 and 30 are modes

Example Which measure of central tendency best represents the data?

Stem	Leaf
9	4 6 8 9 9
10	0 1 2 4 8 9
11	2 2
12	0 1 9|4 = 94

Find the mean, median, and mode.

Mean = 105

Median = 102

Modes = 99 and 112

The median best represents the center of the data since the mean is too high.

Exercises

Find the mean, median, and mode for each data set. Then tell which best represents the data.

1.

Stem	Leaf
2	4 7 7
3	1 2 6 6 6 9
4	0
5	8 8 9 2|4 = 24

2.

Stem	Leaf
9	0 0 1 3 9
10	2 2 5
11	
12	0 3 3 8 8 9 9|0 = 90

3.

Stem	Leaf
5	0 1 9
6	2 2 5 5
7	1 3 5
8	0 3 7 7 5|0 = 50

4.

Month	Days above 90°
May	4
June	7
July	14
August	12
September	8

5.

2-6 Study Guide and Intervention

Probability: Simple Probability and Odds

Probability The **probability** of a **simple event** is a ratio that tells how likely it is that the event will take place. It is the ratio of the number of favorable outcomes of the event to the number of possible outcomes of the event. You can express the probability either as a fraction, as a decimal, or as a percent.

Probability of a Simple Event	For an event a, $P(a) = \dfrac{\text{number of favorable outcomes}}{\text{number of possible outcomes}}$.

Example 1 Mr. Babcock chooses 5 out of 25 students in his algebra class at random for a special project. What is the probability of being chosen?

$P(\text{being chosen}) = \dfrac{\text{number of students chosen}}{\text{total number of students}}$

The probability of being chosen is $\dfrac{5}{25}$ or $\dfrac{1}{5}$.

Example 2 A bowl contains 3 pears, 4 bananas, and 2 apples. If you take a piece of fruit at random, what is the probability that it is *not* a banana?

There are $3 + 4 + 2$ or 9 pieces of fruit.

There are $3 + 2$ or 5 pieces of fruit that are not bananas.

$P(\text{not banana}) = \dfrac{\text{number of other pieces of fruit}}{\text{total number of pieces of fruit}}$

$= \dfrac{5}{9}$

The probability of *not* choosing a banana is $\dfrac{5}{9}$.

Exercises

A card is selected at random from a standard deck of 52 cards. Determine each probability.

1. $P(10)$ **2.** $P(\text{red } 2)$ **3.** $P(\text{king or queen})$

4. $P(\text{black card})$ **5.** $P(\text{ace of spades})$ **6.** $P(\text{spade})$

Two dice are rolled and their sum is recorded. Find each probability.

7. $P(\text{sum is } 1)$ **8.** $P(\text{sum is } 6)$ **9.** $P(\text{sum is less than } 4)$

10. $P(\text{sum is greater than } 11)$ **11.** $P(\text{sum is less than } 15)$ **12.** $P(\text{sum is greater than } 8)$

A bowl contains 4 red chips, 3 blue chips, and 8 green chips. You choose one chip at random. Find each probability.

13. $P(\text{not a red chip})$ **14.** $P(\text{red or blue chip})$ **15.** $P(\text{not a green chip})$

A number is selected at random from the list {1, 2, 3, ..., 10}. Find each probability.

16. $P(\text{even number})$ **17.** $P(\text{multiple of } 3)$ **18.** $P(\text{less than } 4)$

19. A computer randomly chooses a letter from the word *COMPUTER*. Find the probability that the letter is a vowel.

2-6 Study Guide and Intervention (continued)

Probability: Simple Probability and Odds

Odds The odds of an event occurring is the ratio of the number of ways an event can occur (successes) to the number of ways the event cannot occur (failures).

Odds	$\dfrac{\text{number of successes}}{\text{number of failures}}$

Example A die is rolled. Find the odds of rolling a number greater than 4.

The sample space is {1, 2, 3, 4, 5, 6}. Therefore, there are six possible outcomes. Since 5 and 6 are the only numbers greater than 4, two outcomes are successes and four are failures.

So the odds of rolling a number greater than 4 is $\dfrac{2}{4}$, or 1:2.

Exercises

Find the odds of each outcome if the spinner at the right is spun once.

1. multiple of 4

2. odd number

3. even or a 5

4. less than 4

5. even number greater than 5

Find the odds of each outcome if a computer randomly chooses a number between 1 and 20.

6. the number is less than 10

7. the number is a multiple of 4

8. the number is even

9. the number is a one-digit number

A bowl of money at a carnival contains 50 quarters, 75 dimes, 100 nickels, and 125 pennies. One coin is randomly selected.

10. Find the odds that a dime will not be chosen.

11. What are the odds of choosing a quarter if all the dimes are removed?

12. What are the odds of choosing a penny?

Suppose you drop a chip onto the grid at the right. Find the odds of each outcome.

1	2	3	4
5	6	7	8
9	10	11	12
13	14	15	16

13. land on a shaded square

14. land on a square on the diagonal

15. land on square number 16

16. land on a number greater than 12

17. land on a multiple of 5

2-7 Study Guide and Intervention

Square Roots and Real Numbers

Square Roots A **square root** is one of two equal factors of a number. For example, the square roots of 36 are 6 and -6, since $6 \cdot 6$ or 6^2 is 36 and $(-6)(-6)$ or $(-6)^2$ is also 36. A rational number like 36, whose square root is a rational number, is called a **perfect square**.

The symbol $\sqrt{}$ is a **radical sign**. It indicates the nonnegative, or **principal**, square root of the number under the radical sign. So $\sqrt{36} = 6$ and $-\sqrt{36} = -6$. The symbol $\pm\sqrt{36}$ represents both square roots.

Example 1 Find $-\sqrt{\dfrac{25}{49}}$.

$-\sqrt{\dfrac{25}{49}}$ represents the negative square root of $\dfrac{25}{49}$.

$\dfrac{25}{49} = \left(\dfrac{5}{7}\right)^2 \rightarrow -\sqrt{\dfrac{25}{49}} = -\dfrac{5}{7}$

Example 2 Find $\pm\sqrt{0.16}$.

$\pm\sqrt{0.16}$ represents the positive and negative square roots of 0.16.

$0.16 = 0.4^2$ and $0.16 = (-0.4)^2$

$\pm\sqrt{0.16} = \pm 0.4$

Exercises

Find each square root.

1. $\sqrt{64}$

2. $-\sqrt{81}$

3. $\sqrt{16.81}$

4. $\pm\sqrt{100}$

5. $-\sqrt{\dfrac{4}{25}}$

6. $-\sqrt{121}$

7. $\pm\sqrt{\dfrac{25}{144}}$

8. $-\sqrt{\dfrac{25}{16}}$

9. $\pm\sqrt{\dfrac{121}{100}}$

10. $-\sqrt{3600}$

11. $-\sqrt{6.25}$

12. $\pm\sqrt{0.0004}$

13. $\sqrt{\dfrac{144}{196}}$

14. $-\sqrt{\dfrac{36}{49}}$

15. $\pm\sqrt{1.21}$

2-7 # Study Guide and Intervention (continued)

Square Roots and Real Numbers

Classify and Order Numbers Numbers such as $\sqrt{2}$ and $\sqrt{3}$ are not perfect squares. Notice what happens when you find these square roots with your calculator. The numbers continue indefinitely without any pattern of repeating digits. Numbers that cannot be written as a terminating or repeating decimal are called **irrational numbers**. The set of **real numbers** consists of the set of irrational numbers and the set of rational numbers together. The chart below illustrates the various kinds of real numbers.

Natural Numbers	{1, 2, 3, 4, ...}
Whole Numbers	{0, 1, 2, 3, 4, ...}
Integers	{..., −3, −2, −1, 0, 1, 2, 3, ...}
Rational Numbers	{all numbers that can be expressed in the form $\frac{a}{b}$, where a and b are integers and $b \neq 0$}
Irrational Numbers	{all numbers that cannot be expressed in the form $\frac{a}{b}$, where a and b are integers and $b \neq 0$}

Example Name the set or sets of numbers to which each real number belongs.

a. $\frac{4}{11}$ Because 4 and 11 are integers, this number is a rational number.

b. $\sqrt{81}$ Because $\sqrt{81} = 9$, this number is a natural number, a whole number, an integer, and a rational number.

c. $\sqrt{32}$ Because $\sqrt{32} = 5.656854249...$, which is not a repeating or terminating decimal, this number is irrational.

Exercises

Name the set or sets of numbers to which each real number belongs.

1. $\frac{84}{12}$

2. $-\frac{6}{7}$

3. $\frac{2}{3}$

4. $\sqrt{54}$

5. 3.145

6. $\sqrt{25}$

7. 0.62626262...

8. $\sqrt{22.51}$

Write each set of numbers in order from least to greatest.

9. $-\frac{3}{4}, -5, \sqrt{25}, \frac{7}{4}$

10. $\sqrt{0.09}, -0.3131..., \frac{3}{5}$

11. $-1.\overline{25}, 0.05, -\frac{1}{4}, \sqrt{5}$

12. $\frac{5}{4}, -2, \sqrt{124}, -3.11$

13. $-\sqrt{1.44}, -0.35 \frac{1}{5}$

14. $0.\overline{35}, 2\frac{1}{3}, -\frac{9}{5}, \sqrt{5}$

3-1 Study Guide and Intervention

Writing Equations

Write Equations Writing equations is one strategy for solving problems. You can use a variable to represent an unspecified number or measure referred to in a problem. Then you can write a verbal expression as an algebraic expression.

Lesson 3-1

Example 1 Translate each sentence into an equation or a formula.

a. **Ten times a number x is equal to 2.8 times the difference y minus z.**

$10 \times x = 2.8 \times (y - z)$
The equation is $10x = 2.8(y - z)$.

b. **A number m minus 8 is the same as a number n divided by 2.**

$m - 8 = n \div 2$
The equation is $m - 8 = \dfrac{n}{2}$.

c. **The area of a rectangle equals the length times the width. Translate this sentence into a formula.**

Let A = area, ℓ = length, and w = width.
Formula: *Area equals length times width.*
$A = \ell \times w$
The formula for the area of a rectangle is $A = \ell w$.

Example 2 Use the Four-Step Problem-Solving Plan.
The population of the United States in 2001 was about 284,000,000, and the land area of the United States is about 3,500,000 square miles. Find the average number of people per square mile in the United States.
Source: www.census.gov

Step 1 *Explore* You know that there are 284,000,000 people. You want to know the number of people per square mile.

Step 2 *Plan* Write an equation to represent the situation. Let p represent the number of people per square mile.
$3{,}500{,}000 \times p = 284{,}000{,}000$

Step 3 *Solve* $3{,}500{,}000 \times p = 284{,}000{,}000$.
$3{,}500{,}000p = 284{,}000{,}000$ Divide each side by
$p \approx 81.14$ 3,500,000.
There about 81 people per square mile.

Step 4 *Examine* If there are 81 people per square mile and there are 3,500,000 square miles, $81 \times 3{,}500{,}000 = 283{,}500{,}000$, or about 284,000,000 people. The answer makes sense.

Exercises

Translate each sentence into an equation or formula.

1. Three times a number t minus twelve equals forty.

2. One-half of the difference of a and b is 54.

3. Three times the sum of d and 4 is 32.

4. The area A of a circle is the product of π and the radius r squared.

WEIGHT LOSS For Exercises 5–6, use the following information.

Lou wants to lose weight to audition for a part in a play. He weighs 160 pounds now. He wants to weigh 150 pounds.

5. If p represents the number of pounds he wants to lose, write an equation to represent this situation.

6. How many pounds does he need to lose to reach his goal?

3-1 Study Guide and Intervention (continued)

Writing Equations

Write Verbal Sentences You can translate equations into verbal sentences.

Example Translate each equation into a verbal sentence.

a. $4n - 8 = 12$.

$$4n \quad - \quad 8 \quad = \quad 12$$

Four times n minus eight equals twelve.

b. $a^2 + b^2 = c^2$

$$a^2 + b^2 \qquad\qquad = \qquad\qquad c^2$$

The sum of the squares of a and b is equal to the square of c.

Exercises

Translate each equation into a verbal sentence.

1. $4a - 5 = 23$

2. $10 + k = 4k$

3. $6xy = 24$

4. $x^2 + y^2 = 8$

5. $p + 3 = 2p$

6. $b = \frac{1}{3}(h - 1)$

7. $100 - 2x = 80$

8. $3(g + h) = 12$

9. $p^2 - 2p = 9$

10. $C = \frac{5}{9}(F - 32)$

11. $V = \frac{1}{3}Bh$

12. $A = \frac{1}{2}hb$

3-2 Study Guide and Intervention

Solving Equations by Using Addition and Subtraction

Solve Using Addition If the same number is added to each side of an equation, the resulting equation is equivalent to the original one. In general if the original equation involves subtraction, this property will help you solve the equation.

Addition Property of Equality	For any numbers a, b, and c, if $a = b$, then $a + c = b + c$.

Example 1 Solve $m - 32 = 18$.

$m - 32 = 18$	Original equation
$m - 32 + 32 = 18 + 32$	Add 32 to each side.
$m = 50$	Simplify.

The solution is 50.

Example 2 Solve $-18 = p - 12$.

$-18 = p - 12$	Original equation
$-18 + 12 = p - 12 + 12$	Add 12 to each side.
$p = -6$	Simplify.

The solution is -6.

Exercises

Solve each equation. Then check your solution.

1. $h - 3 = -2$

2. $m - 8 = -12$

3. $p - 5 = 15$

4. $20 = y - 8$

5. $k - 0.5 = 2.3$

6. $w - \dfrac{1}{2} = \dfrac{5}{8}$

7. $h - 18 = -17$

8. $-12 = -24 + k$

9. $j - 0.2 = 1.8$

10. $b - 40 = -40$

11. $m - (-12) = 10$

12. $w - \dfrac{3}{2} = \dfrac{1}{4}$

Write an equation for each problem. Then solve the equation and check the solution.

13. Twelve subtracted from a number equals 25. Find the number.

14. What number decreased by 52 equals -12?

15. Fifty subtracted from a number equals eighty. Find the number.

16. What number minus one-half is equal to negative one-half?

17. The difference of a number and eight is equal to 14. What is the number?

18. A number decreased by fourteen is equal to eighteen. What is the number?

Lesson 3-2

3-2 Study Guide and Intervention (continued)

Solving Equations by Using Addition and Subtraction

Solve Using Subtraction If the same number is subtracted from each side of an equation, the resulting equation is equivalent to the original one. In general if the original equation involves addition, this property will help you solve the equation.

Subtraction Property of Equality	For any numbers a, b, and c, if $a = b$, then $a - c = b - c$.

Example Solve $22 + p = -12$.

$$22 + p = -12 \qquad \text{Original equation}$$
$$22 + p - 22 = -12 - 22 \qquad \text{Subtract 22 from each side.}$$
$$p = -34 \qquad \text{Simplify.}$$

The solution is -34.

Exercises

Solve each equation. Then check your solution.

1. $x + 12 = 6$

2. $z + 2 = -13$

3. $-17 = b + 4$

4. $s + (-9) = 7$

5. $-3.2 = \ell + (-0.2)$

6. $-\dfrac{3}{8} + x = \dfrac{5}{8}$

7. $19 + h = -4$

8. $-12 = k + 24$

9. $j + 1.2 = 2.8$

10. $b + 80 = -80$

11. $m + (-8) = 2$

12. $w + \dfrac{3}{2} = \dfrac{5}{8}$

Write an equation for each problem. Then solve the equation and check the solution.

13. Twelve added to a number equals 18. Find the number.

14. What number increased by 20 equals -10?

15. The sum of a number and fifty equals eighty. Find the number.

16. What number plus one-half is equal to four?

17. The sum of a number and 3 is equal to -15. What is the number?

3-3 Study Guide and Intervention

Solving Equations by Using Multiplication and Division

Solve Using Multiplication If each side of an equation is multiplied by the same number, the resulting equation is equivalent to the given one. You can use the property to solve equations involving multiplication and division.

Multiplication Property of Equality	For any numbers a, b, and c, if $a = b$, then $ac = bc$.

Example 1 Solve $3\frac{1}{2}p = 1\frac{1}{2}$.

$3\frac{1}{2}p = 1\frac{1}{2}$ Original equation

$\frac{7}{2}p = \frac{3}{2}$ Rewrite each mixed number as an improper fraction.

$\frac{2}{7}\left(\frac{7}{2}p\right) = \frac{2}{7}\left(\frac{3}{2}\right)$ Multiply each side by $\frac{2}{7}$.

$p = \frac{3}{7}$ Simplify.

The solution is $\frac{3}{7}$.

Example 2 Solve $-\frac{1}{4}n = 16$.

$-\frac{1}{4}n = 16$ Original equation

$-4\left(-\frac{1}{4}n\right) = -4(16)$ Multiply each side by -4.

$n = -64$ Simplify.

The solution is -64.

Exercises

Solve each equation. Then check your solution.

1. $\frac{h}{3} = -2$

2. $\frac{1}{8}m = 6$

3. $\frac{1}{5}p = \frac{3}{5}$

4. $5 = \frac{y}{12}$

5. $-\frac{1}{4}k = -2.5$

6. $-\frac{m}{8} = \frac{5}{8}$

7. $-1\frac{1}{2}h = 4$

8. $-12 = -\frac{3}{2}k$

9. $\frac{j}{3} = \frac{2}{5}$

10. $-3\frac{1}{3}b = 5$

11. $\frac{7}{10}m = 10$

12. $\frac{p}{5} = -\frac{1}{4}$

Write an equation for each problem. Then solve the equation.

13. One-fifth of a number equals 25. Find the number.

14. What number divided by 2 equals -18?

15. A number divided by eight equals 3. Find the number.

16. One and a half times a number equals 6. Find the number.

Lesson 3-3

3-3 Study Guide and Intervention (continued)

Solving Equations by Using Multiplication and Division

Solve Using Division To solve equations with multiplication and division, you can also use the Division Property of Equality. If each side of an equation is divided by the same number, the resulting equation is true.

Division Property of Equality	For any numbers a, b, and c, with $c \neq 0$, if $a = b$, then $\frac{a}{c} = \frac{b}{c}$.

Example 1 Solve $8n = 64$.

$8n = 64$ Original equation
$\frac{8n}{8} = \frac{64}{8}$ Divide each side by 8.
$n = 8$ Simplify.
The solution is 8.

Example 2 Solve $-5n = 60$.

$-5n = 60$ Original equation
$\frac{-5n}{-5} = \frac{60}{-5}$ Divide each side by -5.
$n = -12$ Simplify.
The solution is -12.

Exercises

Solve each equation. Then check your solution.

1. $3h = -42$
2. $8m = 16$
3. $-3t = 51$

4. $-3r = -24$
5. $8k = -64$
6. $-2m = 16$

7. $12h = 4$
8. $-2.4p = 7.2$
9. $0.5j = 5$

10. $-25 = 5m$
11. $6m = 15$
12. $-1.5p = -75$

Write an equation for each problem. Then solve the equation.

13. Four times a number equals 64. Find the number.

14. What number multiplied by -4 equals -16?

15. A number times eight equals -36. Find the number.

3-4 Study Guide and Intervention
Solving Multi-Step Equations

Work Backward Working backward is one of many problem-solving strategies that you can use to solve problems. To work backward, start with the result given at the end of a problem and undo each step to arrive at the beginning number.

Example 1 A number is divided by 2, and then 8 is subtracted from the quotient. The result is 16. What is the number?

Solve the problem by working backward.

The final number is 16. Undo subtracting 8 by adding 8 to get 24. To undo dividing 24 by 2, multiply 24 by 2 to get 48.

The original number is 48.

Example 2 A bacteria culture doubles each half hour. After 3 hours, there are 6400 bacteria. How many bacteria were there to begin with?

Solve the problem by working backward.

The bacteria have grown for 3 hours. Since there are 2 one-half hour periods in one hour, in 3 hours there are 6 one-half hour periods. Since the bacteria culture has grown for 6 time periods, it has doubled 6 times. Undo the doubling by halving the number of bacteria 6 times.

$$6,400 \times \frac{1}{2} \times \frac{1}{2} \times \frac{1}{2} \times \frac{1}{2} \times \frac{1}{2} \times \frac{1}{2} = 6,400 \times \frac{1}{64}$$
$$= 100$$

There were 100 bacteria to begin with.

Exercises

Solve each problem by working backward.

1. A number is divided by 3, and then 4 is added to the quotient. The result is 8. Find the number.

2. A number is multiplied by 5, and then 3 is subtracted from the product. The result is 12. Find the number.

3. Eight is subtracted from a number, and then the difference is multiplied by 2. The result is 24. Find the number.

4. Three times a number plus 3 is 24. Find the number.

5. **CAR RENTAL** Angela rented a car for $29.99 a day plus a one-time insurance cost of $5.00. Her bill was $124.96. For how many days did she rent the car?

6. **MONEY** Mike withdrew an amount of money from his bank account. He spent one fourth for gasoline and had $90 left. How much money did he withdraw?

7. **TELEVISIONS** In 1999, 68% of households with TV's subscribed to cable TV. If 8,000 more subscribers are added to the number of households with cable, the total number of households with cable TV would be 67,600,000. How many households were there with TV in 1999? **Source:** *World Almanac*

Lesson 3-4

3-4 Study Guide and Intervention (continued)

Solving Multi-Step Equations

Solve Multi-Step Equations To solve equations with more than one operation, often called **multi-step equations**, undo operations by working backward. Reverse the usual order of operations as you work.

Example Solve $5x + 3 = 23$.

$5x + 3 = 23$	Original equation.
$5x + 3 - 3 = 23 - 3$	Subtract 3 from each side.
$5x = 20$	Simplify.
$\dfrac{5x}{5} = \dfrac{20}{5}$	Divide each side by 5.
$x = 4$	Simplify.

Exercises

Solve each equation. Then check your solution.

1. $5x + 2 = 27$

2. $6x + 9 = 27$

3. $5x + 16 = 51$

4. $14n - 8 = 34$

5. $0.6x - 1.5 = 1.8$

6. $\dfrac{7}{8}p - 4 = 10$

7. $16 = \dfrac{d - 12}{14}$

8. $8 + \dfrac{3n}{12} = 13$

9. $\dfrac{g}{-5} + 3 = -13$

10. $\dfrac{4b + 8}{-2} = 10$

11. $0.2x - 8 = -2$

12. $3.2y - 1.8 = 3$

13. $-4 = \dfrac{7x - (-1)}{-8}$

14. $8 = -12 + \dfrac{k}{-4}$

15. $0 = 10y - 40$

Write an equation and solve each problem.

16. Find three consecutive integers whose sum is 96.

17. Find two consecutive odd integers whose sum is 176.

18. Find three consecutive integers whose sum is -93.

3-5 Study Guide and Intervention

Solving Equations with the Variable on Each Side

Variables on Each Side To solve an equation with the same variable on each side, first use the Addition or the Subtraction Property of Equality to write an equivalent equation that has the variable on just one side of the equation. Then solve the equation.

Example 1 Solve $5y - 8 = 3y + 12$.

$$5y - 8 = 3y + 12$$
$$5y - 8 - 3y = 3y + 12 - 3y$$
$$2y - 8 = 12$$
$$2y - 8 + 8 = 12 + 8$$
$$2y = 20$$
$$\frac{2y}{2} = \frac{20}{2}$$
$$y = 10$$

The solution is 10.

Example 2 Solve $-11 - 3y = 8y + 1$.

$$-11 - 3y = 8y + 1$$
$$-11 - 3y + 3y = 8y + 1 + 3y$$
$$-11 = 11y + 1$$
$$-11 - 1 = 11y + 1 - 1$$
$$-12 = 11y$$
$$\frac{-12}{11} = \frac{11y}{11}$$
$$-1\frac{1}{11} = y$$

The solution is $-1\frac{1}{11}$.

Exercises

Solve each equation. Then check your solution.

1. $6 - b = 5b + 30$

2. $5y - 2y = 3y + 2$

3. $5x + 2 = 2x - 10$

4. $4n - 8 = 3n + 2$

5. $1.2x + 4.3 = 2.1 - x$

6. $4.4s + 6.2 = 8.8s - 1.8$

7. $\frac{1}{2}b + 4 = \frac{1}{8}b + 88$

8. $\frac{3}{4}k - 5 = \frac{1}{4}k - 1$

9. $8 - 5p = 4p - 1$

10. $4b - 8 = 10 - 2b$

11. $0.2x - 8 = -2 - x$

12. $3y - 1.8 = 3y - 1.8$

13. $-4 - 3x = 7x - 6$

14. $8 + 4k = -10 + k$

15. $20 - a = 10a - 2$

16. $\frac{2}{3}n + 8 = \frac{1}{2}n + 2$

17. $\frac{2}{5}y - 8 = 9 - \frac{3}{5}y$

18. $-4r + 5 = 5 - 4r$

19. $-4 - 3x = 6x - 6$

20. $18 - 4k = -10 - 4k$

21. $12 + 2y = 10y - 12$

Lesson 3-5

3-5 Study Guide and Intervention (continued)

Solving Equations with the Variable on Each Side

Grouping Symbols When solving equations that contain grouping symbols, first use the Distributive Property to eliminate grouping symbols. Then solve.

Example Solve $4(2a - 1) = -10(a - 5)$.

$4(2a - 1) = -10(a - 5)$	Original equation
$8a - 4 = -10a + 50$	Distributive Property
$8a - 4 + 10a = -10a + 50 + 10a$	Add 10a to each side.
$18a - 4 = 50$	Simplify.
$18a - 4 + 4 = 50 + 4$	Add 4 to each side.
$18a = 54$	Simplify.
$\dfrac{18a}{18} = \dfrac{54}{18}$	Divide each side by 18.
$a = 3$	Simplify.

The solution is 3.

Exercises

Solve each equation. Then check your solution.

1. $-3(x + 5) = 3(x - 1)$ **2.** $2(7 + 3t) = -t$ **3.** $3(a + 1) - 5 = 3a - 2$

4. $75 - 9g = 5(-4 + 2g)$ **5.** $5(f + 2) = 2(3 - f)$ **6.** $4(p + 3) = 36$

7. $18 = 3(2c + 2)$ **8.** $3(d - 8) = 3d$ **9.** $5(p + 3) + 9 = 3(p - 2) + 6$

10. $4(b - 2) = 2(5 - b)$ **11.** $1.2(x - 2) = 2 - x$ **12.** $\dfrac{3 + y}{4} = \dfrac{-y}{8}$

13. $\dfrac{a - 8}{12} = \dfrac{2a + 5}{3}$ **14.** $2(4 + 2k) + 10 = k$ **15.** $2(w - 1) + 4 = 4(w + 1)$

16. $6(n - 1) = 2(2n + 4)$ **17.** $2[2 + 3(y - 1)] = 22$ **18.** $-4(r + 2) = 4(2 - 4r)$

19. $-3(x - 8) = 24$ **20.** $4(4 - 4k) = -10 - 16k$ **21.** $6(2 - 2y) = 5(2y - 2)$

3-6 Study Guide and Intervention

Ratios and Proportions

Ratios and Proportions A **ratio** is a comparison of two numbers by division. The ratio of x to y can be expressed as x to y, $x:y$ or $\dfrac{x}{y}$. Ratios are usually expressed in simplest form.

An equation stating that two ratios are equal is called a **proportion**. To determine whether two ratios form a proportion, express both ratios in simplest form or check cross products.

Example 1 Determine whether the ratios $\dfrac{24}{36}$ and $\dfrac{12}{18}$ form a proportion.

$\dfrac{24}{36} = \dfrac{2}{3}$ when expressed in simplest form.

$\dfrac{12}{18} = \dfrac{2}{3}$ when expressed in simplest form.

The ratios $\dfrac{24}{36}$ and $\dfrac{12}{18}$ form a proportion because they are equal when expressed in simplest form.

Example 2 Use cross products to determine whether $\dfrac{10}{18}$ and $\dfrac{25}{45}$ form a proportion.

$\dfrac{10}{18} \overset{?}{=} \dfrac{25}{45}$ Write the proportion.

$10(45) \overset{?}{=} 18(25)$ Cross products

$450 = 450$ Simplify.

The cross products are equal, so $\dfrac{10}{18} = \dfrac{25}{45}$. Since the ratios are equal, they form a proportion.

Exercises

Use cross products to determine whether each pair of ratios forms a proportion.

1. $\dfrac{1}{2}, \dfrac{16}{32}$

2. $\dfrac{5}{8}, \dfrac{10}{15}$

3. $\dfrac{10}{20}, \dfrac{25}{49}$

4. $\dfrac{25}{36}, \dfrac{15}{20}$

5. $\dfrac{12}{32}, \dfrac{3}{16}$

6. $\dfrac{4}{9}, \dfrac{12}{27}$

7. $\dfrac{0.1}{2}, \dfrac{5}{100}$

8. $\dfrac{15}{20}, \dfrac{9}{12}$

9. $\dfrac{14}{21}, \dfrac{20}{30}$

10. $2:3, 20:30$

11. 5 to 9, 25 to 45

12. $\dfrac{72}{64}, \dfrac{9}{8}$

13. $5:5, 30:20$

14. 18 to 24, 50 to 75

15. $100:75, 44:33$

16. $\dfrac{0.05}{1}, \dfrac{1}{20}$

17. $\dfrac{1.5}{2}, \dfrac{6}{8}$

18. $\dfrac{0.1}{0.2}, \dfrac{0.45}{0.9}$

3-6 Study Guide and Intervention (continued)

Ratios and Proportions

Solve Proportions If a proportion involves a variable, you can use cross products to solve the proportion. In the proportion $\frac{x}{5} = \frac{10}{13}$, x and 13 are called **extremes** and 5 and 10 are called **means**. In a proportion, the product of the extremes is equal to the product of the means.

Means-Extremes Property of Proportions	For any numbers a, b, c, and d, if $\frac{a}{b} = \frac{c}{d}$, then $ad = bc$.

Example Solve $\frac{x}{5} = \frac{10}{13}$.

$$\frac{x}{5} = \frac{10}{13} \qquad \text{Original proportion}$$

$$13(x) = 5(10) \qquad \text{Cross products}$$

$$13x = 50 \qquad \text{Simplify.}$$

$$\frac{13x}{13} = \frac{50}{13} \qquad \text{Divide each side by 13.}$$

$$x = 3\frac{11}{13} \qquad \text{Simplify.}$$

The solution is $3\frac{11}{13}$.

Exercises

Solve each proportion.

1. $\dfrac{-3}{x} = \dfrac{2}{8}$

2. $\dfrac{1}{t} = \dfrac{5}{3}$

3. $\dfrac{0.1}{2} = \dfrac{0.5}{x}$

4. $\dfrac{x+1}{4} = \dfrac{3}{4}$

5. $\dfrac{4}{6} = \dfrac{8}{x}$

6. $\dfrac{x}{21} = \dfrac{3}{63}$

7. $\dfrac{9}{y+1} = \dfrac{18}{54}$

8. $\dfrac{3}{d} = \dfrac{18}{3}$

9. $\dfrac{5}{8} = \dfrac{p}{24}$

10. $\dfrac{4}{b-2} = \dfrac{4}{12}$

11. $\dfrac{1.5}{x} = \dfrac{12}{x}$

12. $\dfrac{3+y}{4} = \dfrac{-y}{8}$

13. $\dfrac{a-8}{12} = \dfrac{15}{3}$

14. $\dfrac{12}{k} = \dfrac{24}{k}$

15. $\dfrac{2+w}{6} = \dfrac{12}{9}$

Use a proportion to solve each problem.

16. **MODELS** To make a model of the Guadeloupe River bed, Hermie used 1 inch of clay for 5 miles of the river's actual length. His model river was 50 inches long. How long is the Guadeloupe River?

17. **EDUCATION** Josh finished 24 math problems in one hour. At that rate, how many hours will it take him to complete 72 problems?

3-7 Study Guide and Intervention

Percent of Change

Lesson 3-7

Percent of Change When an increase or decrease in an amount is expressed as a percent, the percent is called the **percent of change**. If the new number is greater than the original number, the percent of change is a **percent of increase**. If the new number is less than the original number, the percent of change is the **percent of decrease**.

Example 1

Find the percent of increase.
   original: 48
   new: 60

First, subtract to find the amount of increase. The amount of increase is $60 - 48 = 12$.

Then find the percent of increase by using the original number, 48, as the base.

$$\frac{12}{48} = \frac{r}{100}$$ Percent proportion

$12(100) = 48(r)$ Cross products

$1200 = 48r$ Simplify.

$$\frac{1200}{48} = \frac{48r}{48}$$ Divide each side by 48.

$25 = r$ Simplify.

The percent of increase is 25%.

Example 2

Find the percent of decrease.
   original: 30
   new: 22

First, subtract to find the amount of decrease. The amount of decrease is $30 - 22 = 8$.

Then find the percent of decrease by using the original number, 30, as the base.

$$\frac{8}{30} = \frac{r}{100}$$ Percent proportion

$8(100) = 30(r)$ Cross products

$800 = 30r$ Simplify.

$$\frac{800}{30} = \frac{30r}{30}$$ Divide each side by 30.

$26\frac{2}{3} = r$ Simplify.

The percent of decrease is $26\frac{2}{3}$%, or about 27%.

Exercises

State whether each percent of change is a percent of increase or a percent of decrease. Then find each percent of change. Round to the nearest whole percent.

1. original: 50
   new: 80

2. original: 90
   new: 100

3. original: 45
   new: 20

4. original: 77.5
   new: 62

5. original: 140
   new: 150

6. original: 135
   new: 90

7. original: 120
   new: 180

8. original: 90
   new: 270

9. original: 27.5
   new: 25

10. original: 84
   new: 98

11. original: 12.5
   new: 10

12. original: 250
   new: 500

NAME _____ DATE _____ PERIOD _____

3-7 Study Guide and Intervention (continued)

Percent of Change

Solve Problems Discounted prices and prices including tax are applications of percent of change. Discount is the amount by which the regular price of an item is reduced. Thus, the discounted price is an example of percent of decrease. Sales tax is amount that is added to the cost of an item, so the price including tax is an example of percent of increase.

Example A coat is on sale for 25% off the original price. If the original price of the coat is $75, what is the discounted price?

The discount is 25% of the original price.

25% of $75 = 0.25 × 75   25% = 0.25

            = 18.75   Use a calculator.

Subtract $18.75 from the original price.

$75 − $18.75 = $56.25

The discounted price of the coat is $56.25.

Exercises

Find the final price of each item. When a discount and a sales tax are listed, compute the discount price before computing the tax.

1. Compact disc: $16
   Discount: 15%

2. Two concert tickets: $28
   Student discount: 28%

3. Airline ticket: $248.00
   Superair discount: 33%

4. Shirt: $24.00
   Sales tax: 4%

5. CD player: $142.00
   Sales tax: 5.5%

6. Celebrity calendar: $10.95
   Sales tax: 7.5%

7. Class ring: $89.00
   Group discount: 17%
   Sales tax: 5%

8. Software: $44.00
   Discount: 21%
   Sales tax: 6%

9. Video recorder: $110.95
   Discount: 20%
   Sales tax: 5%

10. **VIDEOS** The original selling price of a new sports video was $65.00. Due to the demand the price was increased to $87.75. What was the percent of increase over the original price?

11. **SCHOOL** A high school paper increased its sales by 75% when it ran an issue featuring a contest to win a class party. Before the contest issue, 10% of the school's 800 students bought the paper. How many students bought the contest issue?

12. **BASEBALL** Baseball tickets cost $15 for general admission or $20 for box seats. The sales tax on each ticket is 8%, and the municipal tax on each ticket is an additional 10% of the base price. What is the final cost of each type of ticket?

3-8 Study Guide and Intervention

Solving Equations and Formulas

Solve for Variables Sometimes you may want to solve an equation such as $V = \ell wh$ for one of its variables. For example, if you know the values of V, w, and h, then the equation $\ell = \dfrac{V}{wh}$ is more useful for finding the value of ℓ. If an equation that contains more than one variable is to be solved for a specific variable, use the properties of equality to isolate the specified variable on one side of the equation.

Example 1 Solve $2x - 4y = 8$ for y.

$$2x - 4y = 8$$
$$2x - 4y - 2x = 8 - 2x$$
$$-4y = 8 - 2x$$
$$\frac{-4y}{-4} = \frac{8 - 2x}{-4}$$
$$y = \frac{8 - 2x}{-4} \text{ or } \frac{2x - 8}{4}$$

The value of y is $\dfrac{2x - 8}{4}$.

Example 2 Solve $3m - n = km - 8$ for m.

$$3m - n = km - 8$$
$$3m - n - km = km - 8 - km$$
$$3m - n - km = -8$$
$$3m - n - km + n = -8 + n$$
$$3m - km = -8 + n$$
$$m(3 - k) = -8 + n$$
$$\frac{m(3 - k)}{3 - k} = \frac{-8 + n}{3 - k}$$
$$m = \frac{-8 + n}{3 - k}, \text{ or } \frac{n - 8}{3 - k}$$

The value of m is $\dfrac{n - 8}{3 - k}$. Since division by 0 is undefined, $3 - k \neq 0$, or $k \neq 3$.

Exercises

Solve each equation or formula for the variable specified.

1. $ax - b = c$ for x

2. $15x + 1 = y$ for x

3. $(x + f) + 2 = j$ for x

4. $xy + z = 9$ for y

5. $x(4 - k) = p$ for k

6. $7x + 3y = m$ for y

7. $4(c + 3) = t$ for c

8. $2x + b = c$ for x

9. $x(1 + y) = z$ for x

10. $16z + 4x = y$ for x

11. $d = rt$ for r

12. $A = \dfrac{h(a + b)}{2}$ for h

13. $C = \dfrac{5}{9}(F - 32)$ for F

14. $P = 2\ell + 2w$ for w

15. $A = \ell w$ for ℓ

Glencoe Algebra 1

Lesson 3-8

3-8 Study Guide and Intervention *(continued)*

Solving Equations and Formulas

Use Formulas Many real-world problems require the use of formulas. Sometimes solving a formula for a specified variable will help solve the problem.

Example The formula $C = \pi d$ represents the circumference of a circle, or the distance around the circle, where d is the diameter. If an airplane could fly around Earth at the equator without stopping, it would have traveled about 24,900 miles. Find the diameter of Earth.

$C = \pi d$ Given formula

$d = \dfrac{C}{\pi}$ Solve for d.

$d = \dfrac{24{,}900}{3.14}$ Use $\pi = 3.14$.

$d \approx 7930$ Simplify.

The diameter of Earth is about 7930 miles.

Exercises

1. **GEOMETRY** The volume of a cylinder V is given by the formula $V = \pi r^2 h$, where r is the radius and h is the height.

   a. Solve the formula for h.

   b. Find the height of a cylinder with volume 2500π feet and radius 10 feet.

2. **WATER PRESSURE** The water pressure on a submerged object is given by $P = 64d$, where P is the pressure in pounds per square foot, and d is the depth of the object in feet.

   a. Solve the formula for d.

   b. Find the depth of a submerged object if the pressure is 672 pounds per square foot.

3. **GRAPHS** The equation of a line containing the points $(a, 0)$ and $(0, b)$ is given by the formula $\dfrac{x}{a} + \dfrac{y}{b} = 1$.

   a. Solve the equation for y.

   b. Suppose the line contains the points $(4, 0)$, and $(0, -2)$. If $x = 3$, find y.

4. **GEOMETRY** The surface area of a rectangular solid is given by the formula $S = 2\ell w + 2\ell h + 2wh$, where ℓ = length, w = width, and h = height.

   a. Solve the formula for h.

   b. The surface area of a rectangular solid with length 6 centimeters and width 3 centimeters is 72 square centimeters. Find the height.

3-9 Study Guide and Intervention

Weighted Averages

Mixture Problems

Weighted Average	The weighted average M of a set of data is the sum of the product of each number in the set and its weight divided by the sum of all the weights.

Mixture Problems are problems where two or more parts are combined into a whole. They involve weighted averages. In a mixture problem, the weight is usually a price or a percent of something.

Example Delectable Cookie Company sells chocolate chip cookies for $6.95 per pound and white chocolate cookies for $5.95 per pound. How many pounds of chocolate chip cookies should be mixed with 4 pounds of white chocolate cookies to obtain a mixture that sells for $6.75 per pound.

Let w = the number of pounds of chocolate chip cookies

	Number of Pounds	Price per Pound	Total Price
Chocolate Chip	w	6.95	6.95w
White Chocolate	4	5.95	4(5.95)
Mixture	$w + 4$	6.75	6.75($w + 4$)

Equation: $6.95w + 4(5.95) = 6.75(w + 4)$

Solve the equation.

$6.95w + 4(5.95) = 6.75(w + 4)$	Original equation
$6.95w + 23.80 = 6.75w + 27$	Simplify.
$6.95w + 23.80 - 6.75w = 6.75w + 27 - 6.75w$	Subtract 6.75w from each side.
$0.2w + 23.80 = 27$	Simplify.
$0.2w + 23.80 - 23.80 = 27 - 23.80$	Subtract 23.80 from each side.
$0.2w = 3.2$	Simplify.
$w = 16$	Simplify.

16 pounds of chocolate chip cookies should be mixed with 4 pounds of white chocolate cookies.

Exercises

1. **SOLUTIONS** How many grams of sugar must be added to 60 grams of a solution that is 32% sugar to obtain a solution that is 50% sugar?

2. **NUTS** The Quik Mart has two kinds of nuts. Pecans sell for $1.55 per pound and walnuts sell for $1.95 per pound. How many pounds of walnuts must be added to 15 pounds of pecans to make a mixture that sells for $1.75 per pound?

3. **INVESTMENTS** Alice Gleason invested a portion of $32,000 at 9% interest and the balance at 11% interest. How much did she invest at each rate if her total income from both investments was $3,200.

4. **MILK** Whole milk is 4% butterfat. How much skim milk with 0% butterfat should be added to 32 ounces of whole milk to obtain a mixture that is 2.5% butterfat?

3-9 Study Guide and Intervention *(continued)*

Weighted Averages

Uniform Motion Problems Motion problems are another application of weighted averages. **Uniform motion problems** are problems where an object moves at a certain speed, or rate. Use the formula $d = rt$ to solve these problems, where d is the distance, r is the rate, and t is the time.

Example **Bill Gutierrez drove at a speed of 65 miles per hour on an expressway for 2 hours. He then drove for 1.5 hours at a speed of 45 miles per hour on a state highway. What was his average speed?**

$M = \dfrac{65 \cdot 2 + 45 \cdot 1.5}{2 + 1.5}$ Definition of weighted average

≈ 56.4 Simplify.

Bill drove at an average speed of about 56.4 miles per hour.

Exercises

1. **TRAVEL** Mr. Anders and Ms. Rich each drove home from a business meeting. Mr. Anders traveled east at 100 kilometers per hour and Ms. Rich traveled west at 80 kilometers per hours. In how many hours were they 100 kilometers apart.

2. **AIRPLANES** An airplane flies 750 miles due west in $1\frac{1}{2}$ hours and 750 miles due south in 2 hours. What is the average speed of the airplane?

3. **TRACK** Sprinter A runs 100 meters in 15 seconds, while sprinter B starts 1.5 seconds later and runs 100 meters in 14 seconds. If each of them runs at a constant rate, who is further in 10 seconds after the start of the race? Explain.

4. **TRAINS** An express train travels 90 kilometers per hour from Smallville to Megatown. A local train takes 2.5 hours longer to travel the same distance at 50 kilometers per hour. How far apart are Smallville and Megatown?

5. **CYCLING** Two cyclists begin traveling in the same direction on the same bike path. One travels at 15 miles per hour, and the other travels at 12 miles per hour. When will the cyclists be 10 miles apart?

6. **TRAINS** Two trains leave Chicago, one traveling east at 30 miles per hour and one traveling west at 40 miles per hour. When will the trains be 210 miles apart?

4-1 Study Guide and Intervention

The Coordinate Plane

Identify Points In the diagram at the right, points are located in reference to two perpendicular number lines called **axes**. The horizontal number line is the **x-axis**, and the vertical number line is the **y-axis**. The plane containing the x- and y-axes is called the **coordinate plane**. Points in the coordinate plane are named by ordered pairs of the form (x, y). The first number, or **x-coordinate** corresponds to a number on the x-axis. The second number, or **y-coordinate**, corresponds to a number on the y-axis.

The axes divide the coordinate plane into Quadrants I, II, III, and IV, as shown. The point where the axes intersect is called the **origin**. The origin has coordinates (0, 0).

Lesson 4-1

Example 1 Write an ordered pair for point R above.

The x-coordinate is 0 and the y-coordinate is 4. Thus the ordered pair for R is (0, 4).

Example 2 Write ordered pairs for points P and Q above. Then name the quadrant in which each point is located.

The x-coordinate of P is −3 and the y-coordinate is −2. Thus the ordered pair for P is (−3, −2). P is in Quadrant III.

The x-coordinate of Q is 4 and the y-coordinate is −1. Thus the ordered pair for Q is (4, −1). Q is in Quadrant IV.

Exercises

Write the ordered pair for each point shown at the right. Name the quadrant in which the point is located.

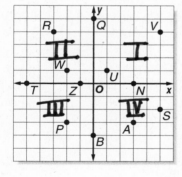

1. N

2. P (−2, −3) III

3. Q

4. R (−3, 4) II

5. S

6. T (−5, 0) x-axis

7. U

8. V (5, 4) I

9. W

10. Z (−1, 0) x-axis

11. A

12. B (0, −4) y-axis

13. Write the ordered pair that describes a point 4 units down from and 3 units to the right of the origin.

14. Write the ordered pair that is 8 units to the left of the origin and lies on the x-axis.

4-1 Study Guide and Intervention *(continued)*

The Coordinate Plane

Graph Points To **graph** an ordered pair means to draw a dot at the point on the coordinate plane that corresponds to the ordered pair. To graph an ordered pair (x, y), begin at the origin. Move left or right x units. From there, move up or down y units. Draw a dot at that point.

Example **Plot each point on a coordinate plane.**

a. $R(-3, 2)$

Start at the origin. Move left 3 units since the x-coordinate is -3. Move up 2 units since the y-coordinate is 2. Draw a dot and label it R.

b. $S(0, -3)$

Start at the origin. Since the x-coordinate is 0, the point will be located on the y-axis. Move down 3 units since the y-coordinate is -3. Draw a dot and label it S.

Exercises

Plot each point on the coordinate plane at the right.

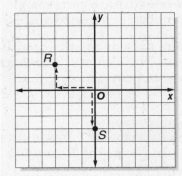

1. $A(2, 4)$ **2.** $B(0, -3)$

3. $C(-4, -4)$ **4.** $D(-2, 0)$

5. $E(1, -4)$ **6.** $F(0, 0)$

7. $G(5, 0)$ **8.** $H(-3, 4)$

9. $I(4, -5)$ **10.** $J(-2, -2)$

11. $K(2, -1)$ **12.** $L(-1, -2)$

13. $M(0, 3)$ **14.** $N(5, -3)$

15. $P(4, 5)$ **16.** $Q(-5, 2)$

4-2 Study Guide and Intervention

Transformations on the Coordinate Plane

Transform Figures **Transformations** are movements of geometric figures. The **preimage** is the position of the figure before the transformation, and the **image** is the position of the figure after the transformation.

Reflection	A figure is flipped over a line.
Translation	A figure is slid horizontally, vertically, or both.
Dilation	A figure is enlarged or reduced.
Rotation	A figure is turned around a point.

Example Determine whether each transformation is a *reflection, translation, dilation,* or *rotation.*

a.   The figure has been flipped over a line, so this is a reflection.

b.   The figure has been turned around a point, so this is a rotation.

c.   The figure has been reduced in size, so this is a dilation.

d.   The figure has been shifted horizontally to the right, so this is a translation.

Exercises

Determine whether each transformation is a *reflection, translation, dilation,* or *rotation.*

1.

2.

3.

4.

5.

6.

Lesson 4-2

4-2 Study Guide and Intervention *(continued)*

Transformations on the Coordinate Plane

Transform Figures on the Coordinate Plane You can perform transformations on a coordinate plane by changing the coordinates of each vertex. The vertices of the image of the transformed figure are indicated by the symbol ', which is read *prime*.

Reflection over *x*-axis	$(x, y) \rightarrow (x, -y)$
Reflection over *y*-axis	$(x, y) \rightarrow (-x, y)$
Translation	$(x, y) \rightarrow (x + a, y + b)$
Dilation	$(x, y) \rightarrow (kx, ky)$
Rotation 90° counterclockwise	$(x, y) \rightarrow (-y, x)$
Rotation 180°	$(x, y) \rightarrow (-x, -y)$

Example A triangle has vertices $A(-1, 1)$, $B(2, 4)$, and $C(3, 0)$. Find the coordinates of the vertices of each image below.

a. reflection over the *x*-axis

To reflect a point over the *x*-axis, multiply the *y*-coordinate by -1.

$A(-1, 1) \rightarrow A'(-1, -1)$
$B(2, 4) \rightarrow B'(2, -4)$
$C(3, 0) \rightarrow C'(3, 0)$

The coordinates of the image vertices are $A'(-1, -1)$, $B'(2, -4)$, and $C'(3, 0)$.

b. dilation with a scale factor of 2

Find the coordinates of the dilated figure by multiplying the coordinates by 2.

$A(-1, 1) \rightarrow A'(-2, 2)$
$B(2, 4) \rightarrow B'(4, 8)$
$C(3, 0) \rightarrow C'(6, 0)$

The coordinates of the image vertices are $A'(-2, 2)$, $B'(4, 8)$, and $C'(6, 0)$.

Exercises

Find the coordinates of the vertices of each figure after the given transformation is performed.

1. triangle *RST* with $R(-2, 4)$, $S(2, 0)$, $T(-1, -1)$ reflected over the *y*-axis

2. triangle *ABC* with $A(0, 0)$, $B(2, 4)$, $C(3, 0)$ rotated about the origin 180°

3. parallelogram *ABCD* with $A(-3, 0)$, $B(-2, 3)$, $C(3, 3)$, $D(2, 0)$ translated 3 units down

4. quadrilateral *RSTU* with $R(-2, 2)$, $S(2, 4)$, $T(4, 4)$, $U(4, 0)$ dilated by a factor of $\frac{1}{2}$

5. triangle *ABC* with $A(-4, 0)$, $B(-2, 3)$, $C(0, 0)$ rotated counterclockwise 90°

6. hexagon *ABCDEF* with $A(0, 0)$, $B(-2, 3)$, $C(0, 4)$, $D(3, 4)$, $E(4, 2)$, $F(3, 0)$ translated 2 units up and 1 unit to the left

4-3 Study Guide and Intervention

Relations

Represent Relations A **relation** is a set of ordered pairs. A relation can be represented by a set of ordered pairs, a table, a graph, or a **mapping**. A mapping illustrates how each element of the domain is paired with an element in the range.

Example 1 Express the relation {(1, 1), (0, 2), (3, −2)} as a table, a graph, and a mapping. State the domain and range of the relation.

x	y
1	1
0	2
3	−2

The domain for this relation is {0, 1, 3}.
The range for this relation is {−2, 1, 2}.

Example 2 A person playing racquetball uses 4 calories per hour for every pound he or she weighs.

a. Make a table to show the relation between weight and calories burned in one hour for people weighing 100, 110, 120, and 130 pounds.
Source: *The Math Teacher's Book of Lists*

x	y
100	400
110	440
120	480
130	520

b. Give the domain and range.
domain: {100, 110, 120, 130}
range: {400, 440, 480, 520}

c. Graph the relation.

Exercises

1. Express the relation {(−2, −1), (3, 3), (4, 3)} as a table, a graph, and a mapping. Then determine the domain and range.

x	y

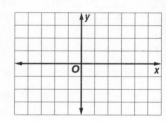

2. The temperature in a house drops 2° for every hour the air conditioner is on between the hours of 6 A.M. and 11 A.M. Make a graph to show the relationship between time and temperature if the temperature at 6 A.M. was 82°F.

Lesson 4-3

4-3 Study Guide and Intervention (continued)

Relations

Inverse Relations The **inverse** of any relation is obtained by switching the coordinates in each ordered pair.

Example **Express the relation shown in the mapping as a set of ordered pairs. Then write the inverse of the relation.**

Relation: {(6, 5), (2, 3), (1, 4), (0, 3)}
Inverse: {(5, 6), (3, 2), (4, 1), (3, 0)}

Exercises

Express the relation shown in each table, mapping, or graph as a set of ordered pairs. Then write the inverse of each relation.

1.

x	y
−2	4
−1	3
2	1
4	5

2.

3.

x	y
−3	5
−2	−1
1	0
2	4

4.

5.

6.

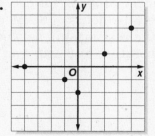

56

4-4 Study Guide and Intervention

Equations as Relations

Solve Equations The equation $y = 3x - 4$ is an example of an **equation in two variables** because it contains two variables, x and y. The **solution** of an equation in two variables is an ordered pair of replacements for the variables that results in a true statement when substituted into the equation.

Example 1 Find the solution set for $y = -2x - 1$, given the replacement set $\{(-2, 3), (0, -1), (1, -2), (3, 1)\}$.

Make a table. Substitute the x and y-values of each ordered pair into the equation.

x	y	y = −2x − 1	True or False
−2	3	$3 = -2(-2) - 1$ $3 = 3$	True
0	−1	$-1 = -2(0) - 1$ $-1 = -1$	True
1	−2	$-2 = -2(1) - 1$ $-2 = -3$	False
3	1	$1 = -2(3) - 1$ $1 = -7$	False

The ordered pairs $(-2, 3)$, and $(0, -1)$ result in true statements. The solution set is $\{(-2, 3), (0, -1)\}$.

Example 2 Solve $b = 2a - 1$ if the domain is $\{-2, -1, 0, 2, 4\}$.

Make a table. The values of a come from the domain. Substitute each value of a into the equation to determine the corresponding values of b in the range.

a	2a − 1	b	(a, b)
−2	$2(-2) - 1$	−5	(−2, −5)
−1	$2(-1) - 1$	−3	(−1, −3)
0	$2(0) - 1$	−1	(0, −1)
2	$2(2) - 1$	3	(2, 3)
4	$2(4) - 1$	7	(4, 7)

The solution set is $\{(-2, -5), (-1, -3), (0, -1), (2, 3), (4, 7)\}$.

Exercises

Find the solution set of each equation, given the replacement set.

1. $y = 3x + 1$; $\{(0, 1), \left(\frac{1}{3}, 2\right), \left(-1, -\frac{2}{3}\right), (-1, -2)\}$

2. $3x - 2y = 6$; $\{(-2, 3), (0, 1), (0, -3), (2, 0)\}$

3. $2x = 5 - y$; $\{(1, 3), (2, 1), (3, 2), (4, 3)\}$

Solve each equation if the domain is $(-4, -2, 0, 2, 4\}$.

4. $x + y = 4$

5. $y = -4x - 6$

6. $5a - 2b = 10$

7. $3x - 2y = 12$

8. $6x + 3y = 18$

9. $4x + 8 = 2y$

10. $x - y = 8$

11. $2x + y = 10$

Glencoe Algebra 1

Lesson 4-4

4-4 **Study Guide and Intervention** *(continued)*

Equations as Relations

Graph Solution Sets You can graph the ordered pairs in the solution set of an equation in two variables. The domain contains values represented by the **independent variable**. The range contains the corresponding values represented by the **dependent variable**, which are determined by the given equation.

Example Solve $4x + 2y = 12$ if the domain is $(-1, 0, 2, 4)$. Graph the solution set.

First solve the equation for y in terms of x.

$$4x + 2y = 12 \qquad \text{Original equation}$$
$$4x + 2y - 4x = 12 - 4x \qquad \text{Subtract } 4x \text{ from each side.}$$
$$2y = 12 - 4x \qquad \text{Simplify.}$$
$$\frac{2y}{2} = \frac{12 - 4x}{2} \qquad \text{Divide each side by 2.}$$
$$y = 6 - 2x \qquad \text{Simplify.}$$

Substitute each value of x from the domain to determine the corresponding value of y in the range.

x	$6 - 2x$	y	(x, y)
-1	$6 - 2(-1)$	8	$(-1, 8)$
0	$6 - 2(0)$	6	$(0, 6)$
2	$6 - 2(2)$	2	$(2, 2)$
4	$6 - 2(4)$	-2	$(4, -2)$

Graph the solution set.

Exercises

Solve each equation for the given domain. Graph the solution set.

1. $x + 2y = 4$ for $x = \{-2, 0, 2, 4\}$

2. $y = -2x - 3$ for $x = \{-2, -1, 0, 1\}$

3. $x - 3y = 6$ for $x = \{-3, 0, 3, 6\}$

4. $2x - 4y = 8$ for $x = \{-4, -2, 0, 2\}$

4-5 Study Guide and Intervention

Graphing Linear Equations

Identify Linear Equations A **linear equation** is an equation that can be written in the form $Ax + By = C$. This is called the **standard form** of a linear equation.

Standard Form of a Linear Equation	$Ax + By = C$, where $A \geq 0$, A and B are not both zero, and A, B, and C are integers whose GCF is 1.

Example 1 Determine whether $y = 6 - 3x$ is a linear equation. If so, write the equation in standard form.

First rewrite the equation so both variables are on the same side of the equation.

$y = 6 - 3x$ Original equation
$y + 3x = 6 - 3x + 3x$ Add 3x to each side.
$3x + y = 6$ Simplify.

The equation is now in standard form, with $A = 3$, $B = 1$ and $C = 6$. This is a linear equation.

Example 2 Determine whether $3xy + y = 4 + 2x$ is a linear equation. If so, write the equation in standard form.

Since the term $3xy$ has two variables, the equation cannot be written in the form $Ax + By = C$. Therefore, this is not a linear equation.

Exercises

Determine whether each equation is a linear equation. If so, write the equation in standard form.

1. $2x = 4y$

2. $6 + y = 8$

3. $4x - 2y = -1$

4. $3xy + 8 = 4y$

5. $3x - 4 = 12$

6. $y = x^2 + 7$

7. $y - 4x = 9$

8. $x + 8 = 0$

9. $-2x + 3 = 4y$

10. $2 + \frac{1}{2}x = y$

11. $\frac{1}{4}y = 12 - 4x$

12. $3xy - y = 8$

13. $6x + 4y - 3 = 0$

14. $yx - 2 = 8$

15. $6a - 2b = 8 + b$

16. $\frac{1}{4}x - 12y = 1$

17. $3 + x + x^2 = 0$

18. $x^2 = 2xy$

Lesson 4-5

4-5 Study Guide and Intervention (continued)

Graphing Linear Equations

Graph Linear Equations The graph of a linear equation is a line. The line represents all solutions to the linear equation. Also, every ordered pair on this line satisfies the equation.

Example Graph the equation $y - 2x = 1$.

Solve the equation for y.

$$y - 2x = 1 \qquad \text{Original equation}$$
$$y - 2x + 2x = 1 + 2x \qquad \text{Add } 2x \text{ to each side.}$$
$$y = 2x + 1 \qquad \text{Simplify.}$$

Select five values for the domain and make a table. Then graph the ordered pairs and draw a line through the points.

x	$2x + 1$	y	(x, y)
-2	$2(-2) + 1$	-3	$(-2, -3)$
-1	$2(-1) + 1$	-1	$(-1, -1)$
0	$2(0) + 1$	1	$(0, 1)$
1	$2(1) + 1$	3	$(1, 3)$
2	$2(2) + 1$	5	$(2, 5)$

Exercises

Graph each equation.

1. $y = 4$

2. $y = 2x$

3. $x - y = -1$

4. $3x + 2y = 6$

5. $x + 2y = 4$

6. $2x + y = -2$

7. $3x - 6y = -3$

8. $-2x + y = -2$

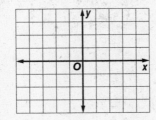

9. $\frac{1}{4}x + \frac{3}{4}y = 6$

4-6 Study Guide and Intervention

Functions

Identify Functions Relations in which each element of the domain is paired with exactly one element of the range are called **functions**.

Example 1 Determine whether the relation {(6, −3), (4, 1), (7, −2), (−3, 1)} is a function. Explain.

Since each element of the domain is paired with exactly one element of the range, this relation is a function.

Example 2 Determine whether $3x - y = 6$ is a function.

Since the equation is in the form $Ax + By = C$, the graph of the equation will be a line, as shown at the right.

If you draw a vertical line through each value of x, the vertical line passes through just one point of the graph. Thus, the line represents a function.

Exercises

Determine whether each relation is a function.

1.

Yes!

2.

Yes!

3.

NO!

4.

NO!

5.

NO!

6.

Yes!

7. {(4, 2), (2, 3), (6, 1)}

Yes!

8. {(−3, −3), (−3, 4), (−2, 4)}

NO!

9. {(−1, 0), (1, 0)}

Yes!

10. $-2x + 4y = 0$

11. $x^2 + y^2 = 8$

12. $x = -4$

4-6 Study Guide and Intervention (continued)

Functions

Function Values Equations that are functions can be written in a form called **function notation**. For example, $y = 2x - 1$ can be written as $f(x) = 2x - 1$. In the function, x represents the elements of the domain, and $f(x)$ represents the elements of the range. Suppose you want to find the value in the range that corresponds to the element 2 in the domain. This is written $f(2)$ and is read "f of 2." The value of $f(2)$ is found by substituting 2 for x in the equation.

Example If $f(x) = 3x - 4$, find each value.

a. $f(3)$

$$f(3) = 3(3) - 4 \qquad \text{Replace } x \text{ with 3.}$$
$$= 9 - 4 \qquad \text{Multiply.}$$
$$= 5 \qquad \text{Simplify.}$$

b. $f(-2)$

$$f(-2) = 3(-2) - 4 \qquad \text{Replace } x \text{ with } -2.$$
$$= -6 - 4 \qquad \text{Multiply.}$$
$$= -10 \qquad \text{Simplify.}$$

Exercises

If $f(x) = 2x - 4$ and $g(x) = x^2 - 4x$, find each value.

1. $f(4)$ **2.** $g(2)$ **3.** $f(-5)$

4. $g(-3)$ **5.** $f(0)$ **6.** $g(0)$

7. $f(3) - 1$ **8.** $f\left(\dfrac{1}{4}\right)$ **9.** $g\left(\dfrac{1}{4}\right)$

10. $f(a^2)$ **11.** $f(k + 1)$ **12.** $g(2c)$

13. $f(3x)$ **14.** $f(2) + 3$ **15.** $g(-4)$

4-7 Study Guide and Intervention

Arithmetic Sequences

Recognize Arithmetic Sequences A **sequence** is a set of numbers in a specific order. If the difference between successive terms is constant, then the sequence is called an **arithmetic sequence**.

Arithmetic Sequence	a numerical pattern that increases or decreases at a constant rate or value called the **common difference**

Example 1 Determine whether the sequence 1, 3, 5, 7, 9, 11, ... is an arithmetic sequence. Justify your answer.

If possible, find the common difference between the terms. Since $3 - 1 = 2$, $5 - 3 = 2$, and so on, the common difference is 2.

Since the difference between the terms of 1, 3, 5, 7, 9, 11, ... is constant, this is an arithmetic sequence.

Example 2 Determine whether the sequence 1, 2, 4, 8, 16, 32, ... is an arithmetic sequence. Justify your answer.

If possible, find the common difference between the terms. Since $2 - 1 = 1$ and $4 - 2 = 2$, there is no common difference.

Since the difference between the terms of 1, 2, 4, 8, 16, 32, ... is not constant, this is not an arithmetic sequence.

Exercises

Determine whether each sequence is an arithmetic sequence. If it is, state the common difference.

1. 1, 5, 9, 13, 17, ...

2. 8, 4, 0, −4, −8, ...

3. 1, 3, 9, 27, 81, ...

4. 10, 15, 25, 40, 60, ...

5. −10, −5, 0, 5, 10, ...

6. 8, 6, 4, 2, 0, −2, ...

7. 4, 8, 12, 16, ...

8. 15, 12, 10, 9, ...

9. 1.1, 2.1, 3.1, 4.1, 5.1, ...

10. 8, 7, 6, 5, 4, ...

11. 0.5, 1.5, 2.5, 3.5, 4.5, ...

12. 1, 4, 16, 64, ...

13. 10, 14, 18, 22, ...

14. −3, −6, −9, −12, ...

15. 7, 0, −7, −14, ...

Lesson 4-7

4-7 Study Guide and Intervention (continued)

Arithmetic Sequences

Write Arithmetic Sequences You can use the common difference of an arithmetic sequence to find the next term of the sequence. Each term after the first term is found by adding the preceding term and the common difference.

Terms of an Arithmetic Sequence	If a_1 is the first term of an arithmetic sequence with common difference d, then the sequence is a_1, $a_1 + d$, $a_1 + 2d$, $a_1 + 3d$, ….
nth Term of an Arithmetic Sequence	$a_n = a_1 + (n - 1)d$

Example 1 Find the next three terms of the arithmetic sequence 28, 32, 36, 40, ….

Find the common difference by subtracting successive terms.

$$28 \quad 32 \quad 36 \quad 40$$
$$+4 \quad +4 \quad +4$$

The common difference is 4.

Add 4 to the last given term, 40, to get the next term. Continue adding 4 until the next three terms are found.

$$40 \quad 44 \quad 48 \quad 52$$
$$+4 \quad +4 \quad +4$$

The next three terms are 44, 48, 52.

Example 2 Write an equation for the nth term of the sequence 12, 15, 18, 21, … .

In this sequence, a_1 is 12. Find the common difference.

$$12 \quad 15 \quad 18 \quad 21$$
$$+3 \quad +3 \quad +3$$

The common difference is 3.

Use the formula for the nth term to write an equation.

$a_n = a_1 + (n - 1)d$	Formula for the nth term
$a_n = 12 + (n - 1)3$	$a_1 = 12, d = 3$
$a_n = 12 + 3n - 3$	Distributive Property
$a_n = 3n + 9$	Simplify.

The equation for the nth term is $a_n = 3n + 9$.

Exercises

Find the next three terms of each arithmetic sequence.

1. 9, 13, 17, 21, 25, …

2. 4, 0, −4, −8, −12, …

3. 29, 35, 41, 47, …

4. −10, −5, 0, 5, …

5. 2.5, 5, 7.5, 10, …

6. 3.1, 4.1, 5.1, 6.1, …

Find the nth term of each arithmetic sequence described.

7. $a_1 = 6, d = 3, n = 10$

8. $a_1 = -2, d = -3, n = 8$

9. $a_1 = 1, d = -5, n = 20$

10. $a_1 = -3, d = -2, n = 50$

11. $a_1 = -12, d = 4, n = 20$

12. $a_1 = 1, d = \frac{1}{2}, n = 11$

Write an equation for the nth term of the arithmetic sequence.

13. 1, 3, 5, 7, …

14. −1, −4, −7, −10, …

15. −4, −9, −14, −19, …

4-8 Study Guide and Intervention

Writing Equations from Patterns

Look for Patterns A very common problem-solving strategy is to **look for a pattern**. Arithmetic sequences follow a pattern, and other sequences can follow a pattern.

 Find the next three terms in the sequence 3, 9, 27, 81, ...

Study the pattern in the sequence.

3   9   27   81
   ×3   ×3   ×3

Successive terms are found by multiplying the last given term by 3.

81   243   729   2187
   ×3   ×3   ×3

The next three terms are 243, 729, 2187.

 Find the next three terms in the sequence 10, 6, 11, 7, 12, 8, ...

Study the pattern in the sequence.

10   6   11   7   12   8
   −4   +5   −4   +5   −4

Assume that the pattern continues.

8   13   9   14
   +5   −4   +5

The next three terms are 13, 9, 14.

Exercises

1. Give the next two items for the pattern below.

Give the next three numbers in each sequence.

2. 2, 12, 72, 432, ...

3. 7, −14, 28, −56, ...

4. 0, 10, 5, 15, 10, ...

5. 0, 1, 3, 6, 10, ...

6. $x - 1, x - 2, x - 3, ...$

7. $x, \dfrac{x}{2}, \dfrac{x}{3}, \dfrac{x}{4}, ...$

Lesson 4-8

4-8 Study Guide and Intervention *(continued)*

Writing Equations from Patterns

Write Equations Sometimes a pattern can lead to a general rule that can be written as an equation.

Example Suppose you purchased a number of packages of blank compact disks. If each package contains 3 compact disks, you could make a chart to show the relationship between the number of packages of compact disks and the number of disks purchased. Use x for the number of packages and y for the number of compact disks.

Make a table of ordered pairs for several points of the graph.

Number of Packages	1	2	3	4	5
Number of CDs	3	6	9	12	15

The difference in the x values is 1, and the difference in the y values is 3. This pattern shows that y is always three times x. This suggests the relation $y = 3x$. Since the relation is also a function, we can write the equation in functional notation as $f(x) = 3x$.

Exercises

1. Write an equation for the function in functional notation. Then complete the table.

x	−1	0	1	2	3	4
y	−2	2	6			

2. Write an equation for the function in functional notation. Then complete the table.

x	−2	−1	0	1	2	3
y	10	7	4			

3. Write an equation in functional notation.

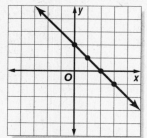

4. Write an equation in functional notation.

5-1 Study Guide and Intervention
Slope

Find Slope

Slope of a Line	$m = \dfrac{\text{rise}}{\text{run}}$ or $m = \dfrac{y_2 - y_1}{x_2 - x_1}$, where (x_1, y_1) and (x_2, y_2) are the coordinates of any two points on a nonvertical line

Example 1 Find the slope of the line that passes through $(-3, 5)$ and $(4, -2)$.

Let $(-3, 5) = (x_1, y_1)$ and $(4, -2) = (x_2, y_2)$.

$m = \dfrac{y_2 - y_1}{x_2 - x_1}$ Slope formula

$= \dfrac{-2 - 5}{4 - (-3)}$ $y_2 = -2, y_1 = 5, x_2 = 4, x_1 = -3$

$= \dfrac{-7}{7}$ Simplify.

$= -1$

Example 2 Find the value of r so that the line through $(10, r)$ and $(3, 4)$ has a slope of $-\dfrac{2}{7}$.

$m = \dfrac{y_2 - y_1}{x_2 - x_1}$ Slope formula

$-\dfrac{2}{7} = \dfrac{4 - r}{3 - 10}$ $m = -\dfrac{2}{7}, y_2 = 4, y_1 = r, x_2 = 3, x_1 = 10$

$-\dfrac{2}{7} = \dfrac{4 - r}{-7}$ Simplify.

$-2(-7) = 7(4 - r)$ Cross multiply.

$14 = 28 - 7r$ Distributive Property

$-14 = -7r$ Subtract 28 from each side.

$2 = r$ Divide each side by -7.

Exercises

Find the slope of the line that passes through each pair of points.

1. $(4, 9), (1, 6)$ 2. $(-4, -1), (-2, -5)$ 3. $(-4, -1), (-4, -5)$

4. $(2, 1), (8, 9)$ 5. $(14, -8), (7, -6)$ 6. $(4, -3), (8, -3)$

7. $(1, -2), (6, 2)$ 8. $(2, 5), (6, 2)$ 9. $(4, 3.5), (-4, 3.5)$

Determine the value of r so the line that passes through each pair of points has the given slope.

10. $(6, 8), (r, -2), m = 1$ 11. $(-1, -3), (7, r), m = \dfrac{3}{4}$ 12. $(2, 8), (r, -4)\ m = -3$

13. $(7, -5), (6, r), m = 0$ 14. $(r, 4), (7, 1), m = \dfrac{3}{4}$ 15. $(7, 5), (r, 9), m = 6$

16. $(10, r), (3, 4), m = -\dfrac{2}{7}$ 17. $(10, 4), (-2, r), m = -0.5$ 18. $(r, 3), (7, r), m = -\dfrac{1}{5}$

Lesson 5-1

5-1 Study Guide and Intervention *(continued)*

Slope

Rate of Change The **rate of change** tells, on average, how a quantity is changing over time. Slope describes a rate of change.

Example **POPULATION** The graph shows the population growth in China.

a. Find the rates of change for 1950–1975 and for 1975–2000.

1950–1975: $\dfrac{\text{change in population}}{\text{change in time}} = \dfrac{0.93 - 0.55}{1975 - 1950}$

$= \dfrac{0.38}{25}$ or 0.0152

1975–2000: $\dfrac{\text{change in population}}{\text{change in time}} = \dfrac{1.24 - 0.93}{2000 - 1975}$

$= \dfrac{0.31}{25}$ or 0.0124

Population Growth in China

People (billions) / Year / 1950 1975 2000 2025*

0.55, 0.93, 1.24, 1.48

*Estimated

Source: United Nations Population Division

b. Explain the meaning of the slope in each case.

From 1950–1975, the growth was 0.0152 billion per year, or 15.2 million per year.
From 1975–2000, the growth was 0.0124 billion per year, or 12.4 million per year.

c. How are the different rates of change shown on the graph?

There is a greater vertical change for 1950–1975 than for 1975–2000. Therefore, the section of the graph for 1950–1975 has a steeper slope.

Exercises

LONGEVITY The graph shows the predicted life expectancy for men and women born in a given year.

1. Find the rates of change for women from 2000–2025 and 2025–2050.

2. Find the rates of change for men from 2000–2025 and 2025–2050.

3. Explain the meaning of your results in Exercises 1 and 2.

4. What pattern do you see in the increase with each 25-year period?

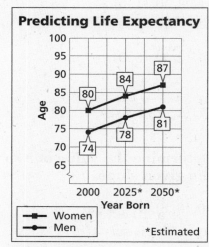

Predicting Life Expectancy

Age / Year Born / 2000 2025* 2050*

80, 84, 87
74, 78, 81

■ Women
● Men

*Estimated

Source: *USA TODAY*

5. Make a prediction for the life expectancy for 2050–2075. Explain how you arrived at your prediction.

5-2 Study Guide and Intervention

Slope and Direct Variation

Direct Variation A **direct variation** is described by an equation of the form $y = kx$, where $k \neq 0$. We say that y *varies directly as* x. In the equation $y = kx$, k is the **constant of variation**.

Example 1 Name the constant of variation for the equation. Then find the slope of the line that passes through the pair of points.

For $y = \frac{1}{2}x$, the constant of variation is $\frac{1}{2}$.

$$m = \frac{y_2 - y_1}{x_2 - x_1} \qquad \text{Slope formula}$$

$$= \frac{1 - 0}{2 - 0} \qquad (x_1, y_1) = (0, 0), (x_2, y_2) = (2, 1)$$

$$= \frac{1}{2} \qquad \text{Simplify.}$$

The slope is $\frac{1}{2}$.

Example 2 Suppose y varies directly as x, and $y = 30$ when $x = 5$.

a. Write a direct variation equation that relates x and y.

Find the value of k.

$$y = kx \qquad \text{Direct variation equation}$$
$$30 = k(5) \qquad \text{Replace } y \text{ with 30 and } x \text{ with 5.}$$
$$6 = k \qquad \text{Divide each side by 5.}$$

Therefore, the equation is $y = 6x$.

b. Use the direct variation equation to find x when $y = 18$.

$$y = 6x \qquad \text{Direct variation equation}$$
$$18 = 6x \qquad \text{Replace } y \text{ with 18.}$$
$$3 = x \qquad \text{Divide each side by 6.}$$

Therefore, $x = 3$ when $y = 18$.

Exercises

Name the constant of variation for each equation. Then determine the slope of the line that passes through each pair of points.

1.

2.

3.

Write a direct variation equation that relates x to y. Assume that y varies directly as x. Then solve.

4. If $y = 4$ when $x = 2$, find y when $x = 16$.

5. If $y = 9$ when $x = -3$, find x when $y = 6$.

6. If $y = -4.8$ when $x = -1.6$, find x when $y = -24$.

7. If $y = \frac{1}{4}$ when $x = \frac{1}{8}$, find x when $y = \frac{3}{16}$.

Lesson 5-2

5-2 Study Guide and Intervention (continued)

Slope and Direct Variation

Solve Problems The **distance formula** $d = rt$ is a direct variation equation. In the formula, distance d varies directly as time t, and the rate r is the constant of variation.

Example

TRAVEL A family drove their car 225 miles in 5 hours.

a. Write a direct variation equation to find the distance traveled for any number of hours.

Use given values for d and t to find r.

$d = rt$	Original equation
$225 = r(5)$	$d = 225$ and $t = 5$
$45 = r$	Divide each side by 5.

Therefore, the direct variation equation is $d = 45t$.

b. Graph the equation.

The graph of $d = 45t$ passes through the origin with slope 45.

$$m = \frac{45}{1} \quad \frac{\text{rise}}{\text{run}}$$

✓**CHECK** (5, 225) lies on the graph.

c. Estimate how many hours it would take the family to drive 360 miles.

$d = 45t$	Original equation
$360 = 45t$	Replace d with 360.
$t = 8$	Divide each side by 45.

Therefore, it will take 8 hours to drive 360 miles.

Exercises

RETAIL The total cost C of bulk jelly beans is $4.49 times the number of pounds p.

1. Write a direct variation equation that relates the variables.

2. Graph the equation on the grid at the right.

3. Find the cost of $\frac{3}{4}$ pound of jelly beans.

CHEMISTRY Charles's Law states that, at a constant pressure, volume of a gas V varies directly as its temperature T. A volume of 4 cubic feet of a certain gas has a temperature of 200° (absolute temperature).

4. Write a direct variation equation that relates the variables.

5. Graph the equation on the grid at the right.

6. Find the volume of the same gas at 250° (absolute temperature).

5-3 Study Guide and Intervention

Slope-Intercept Form

Slope-Intercept Form

Slope-Intercept Form	$y = mx + b$, where m is the given slope and b is the y-intercept

Example 1 **Write an equation of the line whose slope is -4 and whose y-intercept is 3.**

$y = mx + b$ Slope-intercept form
$y = -4x + 3$ Replace m with -4 and b with 3.

Example 2 **Graph $3x - 4y = 8$.**

$3x - 4y = 8$ Original equation
$\quad -4y = -3x + 8$ Subtract $3x$ from each side.
$\quad \dfrac{-4y}{-4} = \dfrac{-3x + 8}{-4}$ Divide each side by -4.
$\quad\quad y = \dfrac{3}{4}x - 2$ Simplify.

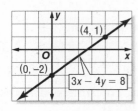

The y-intercept of $y = \dfrac{3}{4}x - 2$ is -2 and the slope is $\dfrac{3}{4}$. So graph the point $(0, -2)$. From this point, move up 3 units and right 4 units. Draw a line passing through both points.

Exercises

Write an equation of the line with the given slope and y-intercept.

1. slope: 8, y-intercept -3 **2.** slope: -2, y-intercept -1 **3.** slope: -1, y-intercept -7

Write an equation of the line shown in each graph.

4.

5.

6.

Graph each equation.

7. $y = 2x + 1$ **8.** $y = -3x + 2$ **9.** $y = -x - 1$

Lesson 5-3

5-3 Study Guide and Intervention (continued)

Slope-Intercept Form

Model Real-World Data

Example **MEDIA** Since 1997, the number of cable TV systems has decreased by an average rate of 121 systems per year. There were 10,943 systems in 1997.

a. Write a linear equation to find the average number of cable systems in any year after 1997.

The rate of change is -121 systems per year. In the first year, the number of systems was 10,943. Let N = the number of cable TV systems. Let x = the number of years after 1997. An equation is $N = -121x + 10,943$.

b. Graph the equation.

The graph of $N = -121x + 10,943$ is a line that passes through the point at $(0, 10,943)$ and has a slope of -121.

c. Find the approximate number of cable TV systems in 2000.

$N = -121x + 10,943$	Original equation
$N = -121(3) + 10,943$	Replace x with 3.
$N = 10,580$	Simplify.

There were about 10,580 cable TV systems in 2000.

Source: *The World Almanac*

Exercises

ENTERTAINMENT In 1995, 65.7% of all households with TV's in the U.S. subscribed to cable TV. Between 1995 and 1999, the percent increased by about 0.6% each year.

1. Write an equation to find the percent P of households that subscribed to cable TV for any year x between 1995 and 1999.

2. Graph the equation on the grid at the right.

3. Find the percent that subscribed to cable TV in 1999.

Source: *The World Almanac*

POPULATION The population of the United States is projected to be 300 million by the year 2010. Between 2010 and 2050, the population is expected to increase by about 2.5 million per year.

4. Write an equation to find the population P in any year x between 2010 and 2050.

5. Graph the equation on the grid at the right.

6. Find the population in 2050.

Source: *The World Almanac*

Glencoe Algebra 1

5-4 Study Guide and Intervention

Writing Equations in Slope-Intercept Form

Write an Equation Given the Slope and One Point

Example 1 Write an equation of a line that passes through $(-4, 2)$ with slope 3.

The line has slope 3. To find the y-intercept, replace m with 3 and (x, y) with $(-4, 2)$ in the slope-intercept form. Then solve for b.

$y = mx + b$ Slope-intercept form
$2 = 3(-4) + b$ $m = 3$, $y = 2$, and $x = -4$
$2 = -12 + b$ Multiply.
$14 = b$ Add 12 to each side.

Therefore, the equation is $y = 3x + 14$.

Example 2 Write an equation of the line that passes through $(-2, -1)$ with slope $\frac{1}{4}$.

The line has slope $\frac{1}{4}$. Replace m with $\frac{1}{4}$ and (x, y) with $(-2, -1)$ in the slope-intercept form.

$y = mx + b$ Slope-intercept form
$-1 = \frac{1}{4}(-2) + b$ $m = \frac{1}{4}$, $y = -1$, and $x = -2$
$-1 = -\frac{1}{2} + b$ Multiply.
$-\frac{1}{2} = b$ Add $\frac{1}{2}$ to each side.

Therefore, the equation is $y = \frac{1}{4}x - \frac{1}{2}$.

Exercises

Write an equation of the line that passes through each point with the given slope.

1.

2.

3.

4. $(8, 2)$, $m = -\frac{3}{4}$

5. $(-1, -3)$, $m = 5$

6. $(4, -5)$, $m = -\frac{1}{2}$

7. $(-5, 4)$, $m = 0$

8. $(2, 2)$, $m = \frac{1}{2}$

9. $(1, -4)$, $m = -6$

10. Write an equation of a line that passes through the y-intercept -3 with slope 2.

11. Write an equation of a line that passes through the x-intercept 4 with slope -3.

12. Write an equation of a line that passes through the point $(0, 350)$ with slope $\frac{1}{5}$.

Lesson 5-4

5-4 # Study Guide and Intervention *(continued)*

Writing Equations in Slope-Intercept Form

Write an Equation Given Two Points

Example Write an equation of the line that passes through $(1, 2)$ and $(3, -2)$.

Find the slope m. To find the y-intercept, replace m with its computed value and (x, y) with $(1, 2)$ in the slope-intercept form. Then solve for b.

$m = \dfrac{y_2 - y_1}{x_2 - x_1}$ Slope formula

$m = \dfrac{-2 - 2}{3 - 1}$ $y_2 = -2, y_1 = 2, x_2 = 3, x_1 = 1$

$m = -2$ Simplify.

$y = mx + b$ Slope-intercept form
$2 = -2(1) + b$ Replace m with -2, y with 2, and x with 1.
$2 = -2 + b$ Multiply.
$4 = b$ Add 2 to each side.

Therefore, the equation is $y = -2x + 4$.

Exercises

Write an equation of the line that passes through each pair of points.

1.

2.

3.

4. $(-1, 6), (7, -10)$ **5.** $(0, 2), (1, 7)$ **6.** $(6, -25), (-1, 3)$

7. $(-2, -1), (2, 11)$ **8.** $(10, -1), (4, 2)$ **9.** $(-14, -2), (7, 7)$

10. Write an equation of a line that passes through the x-intercept 4 and y-intercept -2.

11. Write an equation of a line that passes through the x-intercept -3 and y-intercept 5.

12. Write an equation of a line that passes through $(0, 16)$ and $(-10, 0)$.

5-5 Study Guide and Intervention

Writing Equations in Point-Slope Form

Point-Slope Form

Point-Slope Form	$y - y_1 = m(x - x_1)$, where (x_1, y_1) is a given point on a nonvertical line and m is the slope of the line

Example 1 Write the point-slope form of an equation for a line that passes through (6, 1) and has a slope of $-\frac{5}{2}$.

$y - y_1 = m(x - x_1)$ Point-slope form

$y - 1 = -\frac{5}{2}(x - 6)$ $m = -\frac{5}{2}$; $(x_1, y_1) = (6, 1)$

Therefore, the equation is $y - 1 = -\frac{5}{2}(x - 6)$.

Example 2 Write the point-slope form of an equation for a horizontal line that passes through (4, −1).

$y - y_1 = m(x - x_1)$ Point-slope form

$y - (-1) = 0(x - 4)$ $m = 0$; $(x_1, y_1) = (4, -1)$

$y + 1 = 0$ Simplify.

Therefore, the equation is $y + 1 = 0$.

Exercises

Write the point-slope form of an equation for a line that passes through each point with the given slope.

1.

2.

3.

4. $(2, 1)$, $m = 4$

5. $(-7, 2)$, $m = 6$

6. $(8, 3)$, $m = 1$

7. $(-6, 7)$, $m = 0$

8. $(4, 9)$, $m = \frac{3}{4}$

9. $(-4, -5)$, $m = -\frac{1}{2}$

10. Write the point-slope form of an equation for the horizontal line that passes through $(4, -2)$.

11. Write the point-slope form of an equation for the horizontal line that passes through $(-5, 6)$.

12. Write the point-slope form of an equation for the horizontal line that passes through $(5, 0)$.

Lesson 5-5

5-5 Study Guide and Intervention *(continued)*

Writing Equations in Point-Slope Form

Forms of Linear Equations

Slope-Intercept Form	$y = mx + b$	m = slope; b = y-intercept
Point-Slope Form	$y - y_1 = m(x - x_1)$	m = slope; (x_1, y_1) is a given point.
Standard Form	$Ax + By = C$	A and B are not both zero. Usually A is nonnegative and A, B, and C are integers whose greatest common factor is 1.

Example 1 Write $y + 5 = \frac{2}{3}(x - 6)$ in standard form.

$y + 5 = \frac{2}{3}(x - 6)$ Original equation

$3(y + 5) = 3\left(\frac{2}{3}\right)(x - 6)$ Multiply each side by 3.

$3y + 15 = 2(x - 6)$ Distributive Property
$3y + 15 = 2x - 12$ Distributive Property
$3y = 2x - 27$ Subtract 15 from each side.
$-2x + 3y = -27$ Add $-2x$ to each side.
$2x - 3y = 27$ Multiply each side by -1.

Therefore, the standard form of the equation is $2x - 3y = 27$.

Example 2 Write $y - 2 = -\frac{1}{4}(x - 8)$ in slope-intercept form.

$y - 2 = -\frac{1}{4}(x - 8)$ Original equation

$y - 2 = -\frac{1}{4}x + 2$ Distributive Property

$y = -\frac{1}{4}x + 4$ Add 2 to each side.

Therefore, the slope-intercept form of the equation is $y = -\frac{1}{4}x + 4$.

Exercises

Write each equation in standard form.

1. $y + 2 = -3(x - 1)$

2. $y - 1 = -\frac{1}{3}(x - 6)$

3. $y + 2 = \frac{2}{3}(x - 9)$

4. $y + 3 = -(x - 5)$

5. $y - 4 = \frac{5}{3}(x + 3)$

6. $y + 4 = -\frac{2}{5}(x - 1)$

Write each equation in slope-intercept form.

7. $y + 4 = 4(x - 2)$

8. $y - 5 = \frac{1}{3}(x - 6)$

9. $y - 8 = -\frac{1}{4}(x + 8)$

10. $y - 6 = 3\left(x - \frac{1}{3}\right)$

11. $y + 4 = -2(x + 5)$

12. $y + \frac{5}{3} = \frac{1}{2}(x - 2)$

5-6 Study Guide and Intervention

Geometry: Parallel and Perpendicular Lines

Parallel Lines Two nonvertical lines are **parallel** if they have the same slope. All vertical lines are parallel.

Example **Write the slope-intercept form for an equation of the line that passes through $(-1, 6)$ and is parallel to the graph of $y = 2x + 12$.**

A line parallel to $y = 2x + 12$ has the same slope, 2. Replace m with 2 and (x_1, y_1) with $(-1, 6)$ in the point-slope form.

$y - y_1 = m(x - x_1)$	Point-slope form
$y - 6 = 2(x - (-1))$	$m = 2; (x_1, y_1) = (-1, 6)$
$y - 6 = 2(x + 1)$	Simplify.
$y - 6 = 2x + 2$	Distributive Property
$y = 2x + 8$	Slope-intercept form

Therefore, the equation is $y = 2x + 8$.

Exercises

Write the slope-intercept form for an equation of the line that passes through the given point and is parallel to the graph of each equation.

1.

2.

3.

4. $(-2, 2), y = 4x - 2$

5. $(6, 4), y = \dfrac{1}{3}x + 1$

6. $(4, -2), y = -2x + 3$

7. $(-2, 4), y = -3x + 10$

8. $(-1, 6), 3x + y = 12$

9. $(4, -6), x + 2y = 5$

10. Find an equation of the line that has a y-intercept of 2 that is parallel to the graph of the line $4x + 2y = 8$.

11. Find an equation of the line that has a y-intercept of -1 that is parallel to the graph of the line $x - 3y = 6$.

12. Find an equation of the line that has a y-intercept of -4 that is parallel to the graph of the line $y = 6$.

5-6 Study Guide and Intervention *(continued)*

Geometry: Parallel and Perpendicular Lines

Perpendicular Lines Two lines are **perpendicular** if their slopes are negative reciprocals of each other. Vertical and horizontal lines are perpendicular.

Example Write the slope-intercept form for an equation that passes through $(-4, 2)$ and is perpendicular to the graph of $2x - 3y = 9$.

Find the slope of $2x - 3y = 9$.

$2x - 3y = 9$ Original equation

$\quad -3y = -2x + 9$ Subtract 2x from each side.

$\quad\quad y = \dfrac{2}{3}x - 3$ Divide each side by −3.

The slope of $y = \dfrac{2}{3}x - 3$ is $\dfrac{2}{3}$. So, the slope of the line passing through $(-4, 2)$ that is perpendicular to this line is the negative reciprocal of $\dfrac{2}{3}$, or $-\dfrac{3}{2}$.

Use the point-slope form to find the equation.

$y - y_1 = m(x - x_1)$ Point-slope form

$y - 2 = -\dfrac{3}{2}(x - (-4))$ $m = -\frac{3}{2}; (x_1, y_1) = (-4, 2)$

$y - 2 = -\dfrac{3}{2}(x + 4)$ Simplify.

$y - 2 = -\dfrac{3}{2}x - 6$ Distributive Property

$y = -\dfrac{3}{2}x - 4$ Slope-intercept form

Exercises

Write the slope-intercept form for an equation of the line that passes through the given point and is perpendicular to the graph of each equation.

1. $(4, 2), y = \dfrac{1}{2}x + 1$ **2.** $(2, -3), y = -\dfrac{2}{3}x + 4$ **3.** $(6, 4), y = 7x + 1$

4. $(-8, -7), y = -x - 8$ **5.** $(6, -2), y = -3x - 6$ **6.** $(-5, -1), y = \dfrac{5}{2}x - 3$

7. $(-9, -5), y = -3x - 1$ **8.** $(-1, 3), 2x + 4y = 12$ **9.** $(6, -6), 3x - y = 6$

10. Find an equation of the line that has a y-intercept of -2 and is perpendicular to the graph of the line $x - 2y = 5$.

11. Find an equation of the line that has a y-intercept of 5 and is perpendicular to the graph of the line $4x + 3y = 8$.

NAME _____ DATE _____ PERIOD _____

5-7 Study Guide and Intervention
Scatter Plots and Lines of Fit

Interpret Points on a Scatter Plot A **scatter plot** is a graph in which two sets of data are plotted as ordered pairs in a coordinate plane. If y increases as x increases, there is a **positive correlation** between x and y. If y decreases as x increases, there is a **negative correlation** between x and y. If x and y are not related, there is **no correlation**.

Example **EARNINGS** The graph at the right shows the amount of money Carmen earned each week and the amount she deposited in her savings account that same week. Determine whether the graph shows a positive correlation, a negative correlation, or no correlation. If there is a positive or negative correlation, describe its meaning in the situation.

The graph shows a positive correlation. The more Carmen earns, the more she saves.

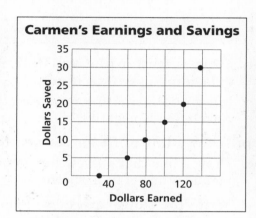

Exercises

Determine whether each graph shows a positive correlation, a negative correlation, or no correlation. If there is a positive correlation, describe it.

1.

Source: The World Almanac

2.

3.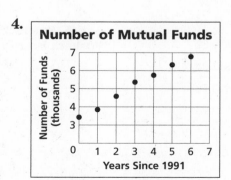

Source: The Wall Street Journal Almanac

4.

Source: The Wall Street Journal Almanac

© Glencoe/McGraw-Hill   79   Glencoe Algebra 1

5-7 Study Guide and Intervention (continued)

Scatter Plots and Lines of Fit

Lines of Fit

Example The table below shows the number of students per computer in United States public schools for certain school years from 1990 to 2000.

Year	1990	1992	1994	1996	1998	2000
Students per Computer	22	18	14	10	6.1	5.4

a. Draw a scatter plot and determine what relationship exists, if any.

Since y decreases as x increases, the correlation is negative.

b. Draw a line of fit for the scatter plot.

Draw a line that passes close to most of the points. A line of fit is shown.

c. Write the slope-intercept form of an equation for the line of fit.

The line of fit shown passes through (1993, 16) and (1999, 5.7). Find the slope.

$$m = \frac{5.7 - 16}{1999 - 1993}$$

$$m = -1.7$$

Find b in $y = -1.7x + b$.

$$16 = -1.7 \cdot 1993 + b$$

$$3404 = b$$

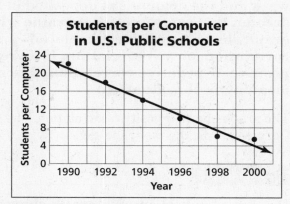

Source: *The World Almanac*

Therefore, an equation of a line of fit is $y = -1.7x + 3404$.

Exercises

Refer to the table for Exercises 1–3.

Years Since 1995	Hourly Wage
0	$11.43
1	$11.82
2	$12.28
3	$12.78
4	$13.24

1. Draw a scatter plot.

2. Draw a line of fit for the data.

3. Write the slope-intercept form of an equation for the line of fit.

Source: *The World Almanac*

Glencoe Algebra 1

6-1 Study Guide and Intervention

Solving Inequalities by Addition and Subtraction

Solve Inequalities by Addition Addition can be used to solve inequalities. If any number is added to each side of a true inequality, the resulting inequality is also true.

Addition Property of Inequalities	For all numbers a, b, and c, if $a > b$, then $a + c > b + c$, and if $a < b$, then $a + c < b + c$.

The property is also true when $>$ and $<$ are replaced with $\geq$ and $\leq$.

Example 1 Solve $x - 8 \leq -6$. Then graph it on a number line.

$x - 8 \leq -6$	Original inequality
$x - 8 + 8 \leq -6 + 8$	Add 8 to each side.
$x \leq 2$	Simplify.

The solution in set-builder notation is $\{x \mid x \leq 2\}$.

Number line graph:

Example 2 Solve $4 - 2a > -a$. Then graph it on a number line.

$4 - 2a > -a$	Original inequality
$4 - 2a + 2a > -a + 2a$	Add 2a to each side.
$4 > a$	Simplify.
$a < 4$	$4 > a$ is the same as $a < 4$.

The solution in set-builder notation is $\{a \mid a < 4\}$.

Number line graph:

Exercises

Solve each inequality. Then check your solution, and graph it on a number line.

1. $t - 12 \geq 16$

2. $n - 12 < 6$

3. $6 \leq g - 3$

4. $n - 8 < -13$

5. $-12 > -12 + y$

6. $-6 > s - 8$

Solve each inequality. Then check your solution.

7. $-3x \leq 8 - 4x$

8. $0.6n \geq 12 - 0.4n$

9. $-8k - 12 < -9k$

10. $-y - 10 > 15 - 2y$

11. $z - \dfrac{1}{3} \leq \dfrac{4}{3}$

12. $-2b > -4 - 3b$

Define a variable, write an inequality, and solve each problem. Then check your solution.

13. A number decreased by 4 is less than 14.

14. The difference of two numbers is more than 12, and one of the numbers is 3.

15. Forty is no greater than the difference of a number and 2.

6-1 Study Guide and Intervention *(continued)*

Solving Inequalities by Addition and Subtraction

Solve Inequalities by Subtraction Subtraction can be used to solve inequalities. If any number is subtracted from each side of a true inequality, the resulting inequality is also true.

Subtraction Property of Inequalities	For all numbers a, b, and c, if $a > b$, then $a - c > b - c$, and if $a < b$, then $a - c < b - c$.

The property is also true when $>$ and $<$ are replaced with $\geq$ and $\leq$.

Example Solve $3a + 5 > 4 + 2a$. Then graph it on a number line.

$$3a + 5 > 4 + 2a \qquad \text{Original inequality}$$
$$3a + 5 - 2a > 4 + 2a - 2a \qquad \text{Subtract } 2a \text{ from each side.}$$
$$a + 5 > 4 \qquad \text{Simplify.}$$
$$a + 5 - 5 > 4 - 5 \qquad \text{Subtract 5 from each side.}$$
$$a > -1 \qquad \text{Simplify.}$$

The solution is $\{a \mid a > -1\}$.

Number line graph:

```
<---+---+---+---o---+---+---+---+---+--->
   -4  -3  -2  -1   0   1   2   3   4
```

Exercises

Solve each inequality. Then check your solution, and graph it on a number line.

1. $t + 12 \geq 8$

2. $n + 12 > -12$

3. $16 \leq h + 9$

4. $y + 4 > -2$

5. $3r + 6 > 4r$

6. $\dfrac{3}{2}q - 5 \geq \dfrac{1}{2}q$

Solve each inequality. Then check your solution.

7. $4p \geq 3p + 0.7$

8. $r + \dfrac{1}{4} > \dfrac{3}{8}$

9. $9k + 12 > 8k$

10. $-1.2 > 2.4 + y$

11. $4y < 5y + 14$

12. $3n + 17 < 4n$

Define a variable, write an inequality, and solve each problem. Then check your solution.

13. The sum of a number and 8 is less than 12.

14. The sum of two numbers is at most 6, and one of the number is -2.

15. The sum of a number and 6 is greater than or equal to -4.

6-2 Study Guide and Intervention

Solving Inequalities by Multiplication and Division

Solve Inequalities by Multiplication If each side of an inequality is multiplied by the same positive number, the resulting inequality is also true. However, if each side of an inequality is multiplied by the same negative number, the direction of the inequality must be reversed for the resulting inequality to be true.

Multiplication Property of Inequalities	For all numbers a, b, and c, with $c \neq 0$,
	1. if c is positive and $a > b$, then $ac > bc$;
	    if c is positive and $a < b$, then $ac < bc$;
	2. if c is negative and $a > b$, then $ac < bc$;
	    if c is negative and $a < b$, then $ac > bc$.

The property is also true when $>$ and $<$ are replaced with $\geq$ and $\leq$.

Example 1 Solve $-\dfrac{y}{8} \geq 12$.

$-\dfrac{y}{8} \geq 12$ Original equation

$(-8)\left(-\dfrac{y}{8}\right) \leq (-8)12$ Multiply each side by -8; change $\geq$ to $\leq$.

$y \leq -96$ Simplify.

The solution is $\{y \mid y \leq -96\}$.

Example 2 Solve $\dfrac{3}{4}k < 15$.

$\dfrac{3}{4}k < 15$ Original equation

$\left(\dfrac{4}{3}\right)\dfrac{3}{4}k < \left(\dfrac{4}{3}\right)15$ Multiply each side by $\frac{4}{3}$.

$k < 20$ Simplify.

The solution is $\{k \mid k < 20\}$.

Exercises

Solve each inequality. Then check your solution.

1. $\dfrac{y}{6} \leq 2$ **2.** $-\dfrac{n}{50} > 22$ **3.** $\dfrac{3}{5}h \geq -3$ **4.** $-\dfrac{p}{6} < -6$

5. $\dfrac{1}{4}n \geq 10$ **6.** $-\dfrac{2}{3}b < \dfrac{1}{3}$ **7.** $\dfrac{3m}{5} < -\dfrac{3}{20}$ **8.** $-2.51 \leq -\dfrac{2h}{4}$

9. $\dfrac{g}{5} \geq -2$ **10.** $-\dfrac{3}{4} > -\dfrac{9p}{5}$ **11.** $\dfrac{n}{10} \geq 5.4$ **12.** $\dfrac{2a}{7} \geq -6$

Define a variable, write an inequality, and solve each problem. Then check your solution.

13. Half of a number is at least 14.

14. The opposite of one-third a number is greater than 9.

15. One fifth of a number is at most 30.

Lesson 6-2

6-2 Study Guide and Intervention *(continued)*

Solving Inequalities by Multiplication and Division

Solve Inequalities by Division If each side of a true inequality is divided by the same positive number, the resulting inequality is also true. However, if each side of an inequality is divided by the same negative number, the direction of the inequality symbol must be reversed for the resulting inequality to be true.

Division Property of Inequalities	For all numbers a, b, and c with $c \neq 0$,
	1. if c is positive and $a > b$, then $\frac{a}{c} > \frac{b}{c}$; if c is positive and $a < b$, then $\frac{a}{c} < \frac{b}{c}$;
	2. if c is negative and $a > b$, then $\frac{a}{c} < \frac{b}{c}$; if c is negative and $a < b$, then $\frac{a}{c} > \frac{b}{c}$.

The property is also true when $>$ and $<$ are replaced with $\geq$ and $\leq$.

Example **Solve $-12y \geq 48$.**

$-12y \geq 48$ Original inequality

$\dfrac{-12y}{-12} \leq \dfrac{48}{-12}$ Divide each side by -12 and change $\geq$ to $\leq$.

$y \leq -4$ Simplify.

The solution is $\{y \mid y \leq -4\}$.

Exercises

Solve each inequality. Then check your solution.

1. $25g \geq -100$ **2.** $-2x \geq 9$ **3.** $-5c > 2$ **4.** $-8m < -64$

5. $-6k < \dfrac{1}{5}$ **6.** $18 < -3b$ **7.** $30 < -3n$ **8.** $-0.24 < 0.6w$

9. $25 \geq -2m$ **10.** $-30 > -5p$ **11.** $-2n \geq 6.2$ **12.** $-35 < 0.05h$

13. $-40 > 10h$ **14.** $-\dfrac{2}{3}n \geq 6$ **15.** $-3 < \dfrac{p}{4}$

Define a variable, write an inequality, and solve each problem. Then check your solution.

16. Four times a number is no more than 108.

17. The opposite of three times a number is greater than 12.

18. Negative five times a number is at most 100.

6-3 Study Guide and Intervention
Solving Multi-Step Inequalities

Solve Multi-Step Inequalities To solve linear inequalities involving more than one operation, undo the operations in reverse of the order of operations, just as you would solve an equation with more than one operation.

Example 1 Solve $6x - 4 \le 2x + 12$.

$6x - 4 \le 2x + 12$	Original inequality
$6x - 4 - 2x \le 2x + 12 - 2x$	Subtract 2x from each side.
$4x - 4 \le 12$	Simplify.
$4x - 4 + 4 \le 12 + 4$	Add 4 to each side.
$4x \le 16$	Simplify.
$\dfrac{4x}{4} \le \dfrac{16}{4}$	Divide each side by 4.
$x \le 4$	Simplify.

The solution is $\{x \mid x \le 4\}$.

Example 2 Solve $3a - 15 > 4 + 5a$.

$3a - 15 > 4 + 5a$	Original inequality
$3a - 15 - 5a > 4 + 5a - 5a$	Subtract 5a from each side.
$-2a - 15 > 4$	Simplify.
$-2a - 15 + 15 > 4 + 15$	Add 15 to each side.
$-2a > 19$	Simplify.
$\dfrac{-2a}{-2} < \dfrac{19}{-2}$	Divide each side by −2 and change > to <.
$a < -9\dfrac{1}{2}$	Simplify.

The solution is $\left\{a \mid a < -9\dfrac{1}{2}\right\}$.

Exercises

Solve each inequality. Then check your solution.

1. $11y + 13 \ge -1$

2. $8n - 10 < 6 - 2n$

3. $\dfrac{q}{7} + 1 > -5$

4. $6n + 12 < 8 + 8n$

5. $-12 - d > -12 + 4d$

6. $5r - 6 > 8r - 18$

7. $\dfrac{-3x + 6}{2} \le 12$

8. $7.3y - 14.4 > 4.9y$

9. $-8m - 3 < 18 - m$

10. $-4y - 10 > 19 - 2y$

11. $9n - 24n + 45 > 0$

12. $\dfrac{4x - 2}{5} \ge -4$

Define a variable, write an inequality, and solve each problem. Then check your solution.

13. Negative three times a number plus four is no more than the number minus eight.

14. One fourth of a number decreased by three is at least two.

15. The sum of twelve and a number is no greater than the sum of twice the number and −8.

Lesson 6-3

6-3 Study Guide and Intervention (continued)

Solving Multi-Step Inequalities

Solve Inequalities Involving the Distributive Property When solving inequalities that contain grouping symbols, first use the Distributive Property to remove the grouping symbols. Then undo the operations in reverse of the order of operations, just as you would solve an equation with more than one operation.

Example Solve $3a - 2(6a - 4) > 4 - (4a + 6)$.

$3a - 2(6a - 4) > 4 - (4a + 6)$	Original inequality
$3a - 12a + 8 > 4 - 4a - 6$	Distributive Property
$-9a + 8 > -2 - 4a$	Combine like terms.
$-9a + 8 + 4a > -2 - 4a + 4a$	Add 4a to each side.
$-5a + 8 > -2$	Combine like terms.
$-5a + 8 - 8 > -2 - 8$	Subtract 8 from each side.
$-5a > -10$	Simplify.
$a < 2$	Divide each side by -5 and change $>$ to $<$.

The solution in set-builder notation is $\{a \mid a < 2\}$.

Exercises

Solve each inequality. Then check your solution.

1. $2(t + 3) \geq 16$ **2.** $3(d - 2) - 2d > 16$ **3.** $4h - 8 < 2(h - 1)$

4. $6y + 10 > 8 - (y + 14)$ **5.** $4.6(x - 3.4) > 5.1x$ **6.** $-5x - (2x + 3) \geq 1$

7. $3(2y - 4) - 2(y + 1) > 10$ **8.** $8 - 2(b + 1) < 12 - 3b$ **9.** $-2(k - 1) > 8(1 + k)$

10. $0.3(y - 2) > 0.4(1 + y)$ **11.** $m + 17 \leq -(4m - 13)$

12. $3n + 8 \leq 2(n - 4) - 2(1 - n)$ **13.** $2(y - 2) > -4 + 2y$

14. $k - 17 \leq -(17 - k)$ **15.** $n - 4 \leq -3(2 + n)$

Define a variable, write an inequality, and solve each problem. Then check your solution.

16. Twice the sum of a number and 4 is less than 12.

17. Three times the sum of a number and six is greater than four times the number decreased by two.

18. Twice the difference of a number and four is less than the sum of the number and five.

6-4 Study Guide and Intervention

Solving Compound Inequalities

Inequalities Containing and A compound inequality containing *and* is true only if both inequalities are true. The graph of a compound inequality containing *and* is the **intersection** of the graphs of the two inequalities. Every solution of the compound inequality must be a solution of both inequalities.

Example 1 **Graph the solution set of $x < 2$ and $x \geq -1$.**

Graph $x < 2$.

Graph $x \geq -1$.

Find the intersection.

The solution set is $\{x \mid -1 \leq x < 2\}$.

Example 2 **Solve $-1 < x + 2 < 3$ using *and*. Then graph the solution set.**

$$-1 < x + 2 \qquad \text{and} \qquad x + 2 < 3$$
$$-1 - 2 < x + 2 - 2 \qquad\qquad x + 2 - 2 < 3 - 2$$
$$-3 < x \qquad\qquad\qquad x < 1$$

Graph $x > -3$.

Graph $x < 1$.

Find the intersection.

The solution set is $\{x \mid -3 < x < 1\}$.

Exercises

Graph the solution set of each compound inequality.

1. $b > -1$ and $b \leq 3$

$-4\ -3\ -2\ -1\ \ 0\ \ 1\ \ 2\ \ 3\ \ 4$

2. $2 \geq q \geq -5$

$-6\ -5\ -4\ -3\ -2\ -1\ \ 0\ \ 1\ \ 2$

3. $x > -3$ and $x \leq 4$

$-4\ -3\ -2\ -1\ \ 0\ \ 1\ \ 2\ \ 3\ \ 4$

4. $-2 \leq p < 4$

$-3\ -2\ -1\ \ 0\ \ 1\ \ 2\ \ 3\ \ 4\ \ 5$

5. $-3 < d$ and $d < 2$

$-4\ -3\ -2\ -1\ \ 0\ \ 1\ \ 2\ \ 3\ \ 4$

6. $-1 \leq p \leq 3$

$-4\ -3\ -2\ -1\ \ 0\ \ 1\ \ 2\ \ 3\ \ 4$

Solve each compound inequality. Then graph the solution set.

7. $4 < w + 3 \leq 5$

$-4\ -3\ -2\ -1\ \ 0\ \ 1\ \ 2\ \ 3\ \ 4$

8. $-3 \leq p - 5 < 2$

$0\ \ 1\ \ 2\ \ 3\ \ 4\ \ 5\ \ 6\ \ 7\ \ 8$

9. $-4 < x + 2 \leq -2$

$-7\ -6\ -5\ -4\ -3\ -2\ -1\ \ 0\ \ 1$

10. $y - 1 < 2$ and $y + 2 \geq 1$

$-4\ -3\ -2\ -1\ \ 0\ \ 1\ \ 2\ \ 3\ \ 4$

11. $n - 2 > -3$ and $n + 4 < 6$

$-4\ -3\ -2\ -1\ \ 0\ \ 1\ \ 2\ \ 3\ \ 4$

12. $d - 3 < 6d + 12 < 2d + 32$

$-3\ -2\ -1\ \ 0\ \ 1\ \ 2\ \ 3\ \ 4\ \ 5$

Lesson 6-4

6-4 **Study Guide and Intervention** *(continued)*

Solving Compound Inequalities

Inequalities Containing *or* A compound inequality containing *or* is true if one or both of the inequalities are true. The graph of a compound inequality containing *or* is the **union** of the graphs of the two inequalities. The union can be found by graphing both inequalities on the same number line. A solution of the compound inequality is a solution of either inequality, not necessarily both.

Example Solve $2a + 1 < 11$ or $a > 3a + 2$.

$$2a + 1 < 11 \qquad \text{or} \qquad a > 3a + 2$$
$$2a + 1 - 1 < 11 - 1 \qquad a - 3a > 3a - 3a + 2$$
$$2a < 10 \qquad\qquad -2a > 2$$
$$\frac{2a}{2} < \frac{10}{2} \qquad\qquad \frac{-2a}{-2} < \frac{2}{-2}$$
$$a < 5 \qquad\qquad a < -1$$

Graph $a < 5$.

Graph $a < -1$.

Find the union.

The solution set is $\{a \mid a < 5\}$.

Exercises

Graph the solution set of each compound inequality.

1. $b > 2$ or $b \le -3$

2. $3 \ge q$ or $q \le 1$

3. $y \le -4$ or $y > 0$

4. $4 \le p$ or $p < 8$

5. $-3 < d$ or $d < 2$

6. $-2 \le x$ or $3 \le x$

Solve each compound inequality. Then graph the solution set.

7. $3 < 3w$ or $3w \ge 9$

8. $-3p + 1 \le -11$ or $p < 2$

9. $2x + 4 \le 6$ or $x \ge 2x - 4$

10. $2y + 2 < 12$ or $y - 3 \ge 2y$

11. $\frac{1}{2}n > -2$ or $2n - 2 < 6 + n$

12. $3a + 2 \ge 5$ or $7 + 3a < 2a + 6$

NAME _____ DATE _____ PERIOD _____

6-5 Study Guide and Intervention

Solving Open Sentences Involving Absolute Value

Absolute Value Equations When solving equations that involve absolute value, there are two cases to consider.

Case 1: The value inside the absolute value symbols is positive.
Case 2: The value inside the absolute value symbols is negative.

Example 1 Solve $|x + 4| = 1$. Then graph the solution set.

Write $|x + 4 = 1|$ as $x + 4 = 1$ or $x + 4 = -1$.

$$x + 4 = 1 \quad\quad \text{or} \quad\quad x + 4 = -1$$
$$x + 4 - 4 = 1 - 4 \quad\quad\quad x + 4 = -1$$
$$x = -3 \quad\quad\quad x + 4 - 4 = -1 - 4$$
$$x = -5$$

The solution set is $\{-5, -3\}$.
The graph is shown below.

-8 -7 -6 -5 -4 -3 -2 -1 0

Example 2 Write an inequality involving absolute value for the graph.

-3 -2 -1 0 1 2 3 4 5

Find the point that is the same distance from -2 as it is from 4.

3 units   3 units
-3 -2 -1 0 1 2 3 4 5

The distance from 1 to -2 is 3 units. The distance from 1 to 4 is 3 units.
So, $|x - 1| = 3$.

Exercises

Solve each open sentence. Then graph the solution set.

1. $|y| = 3$

-4 -3 -2 -1 0 1 2 3 4

2. $|x - 4| = 4$

0 1 2 3 4 5 6 7 8

3. $|y + 3| = 2$

-8 -7 -6 -5 -4 -3 -2 -1 0

4. $|b + 2| = 3$

-6 -5 -4 -3 -2 -1 0 1 2

5. $|w - 2| = 5$

-8 -6 -4 -2 0 2 4 6 8

6. $|t + 2| = 4$

-8 -6 -4 -2 0 2 4 6 8

7. $|2x| = 8$

-4 -3 -2 -1 0 1 2 3 4

8. $|5y - 2| = 7$

-4 -3 -2 -1 0 1 2 3 4

9. $|p - 0.2| = 0.5$

-0.8   -0.4   0   0.4   0.8

10. $|d - 100| = 50$

50   100   150   200

11. $|2x - 1| = 11$

-6 -4 -2 0 2 4 6 8 10

12. $\left|3x + \dfrac{1}{2}\right| = 6$

-3 -2 -1 0 1 2 3 4 5

For each graph, write an open sentence involving absolute value.

13.
-8 -6 -4 -2 0 2 4 6 8

14.
-4 -3 -2 -1 0 1 2 3 4

15.
-7 -6 -5 -4 -3 -2 -1 0 1

Lesson 6-5

6-5 Study Guide and Intervention *(continued)*

Solving Open Sentences Involving Absolute Value

Absolute Value Inequalities When solving inequalities that involve absolute value, there are two cases to consider for inequalities involving < (or ≤) and two cases to consider for inequalities involving > (or ≥).

If $\lvert x \rvert < n$, then $x > -n$ and $x < n$.
If $\lvert x \rvert > n$, then $x > n$ or $x < -n$.

Remember that inequalities with *and* are related to intersections, while inequalities with *or* are related to unions.

Example **Solve $\lvert 3a + 4 \rvert < 10$. Then graph the solution set.**

Write $\lvert 3a + 4 \rvert < 10$ as $3a + 4 < 10$ and $3a + 4 > -10$.

$$3a + 4 < 10 \quad \text{and} \quad 3a + 4 > -10$$
$$3a + 4 - 4 < 10 - 4 \qquad 3a + 4 - 4 > -10 - 4$$
$$3a < 6 \qquad 3a > -14$$
$$\frac{3a}{3} < \frac{6}{3} \qquad \frac{3a}{3} > \frac{-14}{3}$$
$$a < 2 \qquad a > -4\frac{2}{3}$$

The solution set is $\left\{ a \mid -4\frac{2}{3} < a < 2 \right\}$.

Now graph the solution set.

(number line: −5 −4 −3 −2 −1 0 1 2 3)

Exercises

Solve each open sentence. Then graph the solution set.

1. $\lvert c - 2 \rvert > 6$

−6 −4 −2 0 2 4 6 8 10

2. $\lvert x - 9 \rvert < 0$

−4 −3 −2 −1 0 1 2 3 4

3. $\lvert 3f + 10 \rvert \leq 4$

−6 −5 −4 −3 −2 −1 0 1 2

4. $\lvert x \rvert \leq 2$

−4 −3 −2 −1 0 1 2 3 4

5. $\lvert x \rvert \geq 3$

−4 −3 −2 −1 0 1 2 3 4

6. $\lvert 2x + 1 \rvert \geq -2$

−4 −3 −2 −1 0 1 2 3 4

7. $\lvert 2d - 1 \rvert \leq 4$

−4 −3 −2 −1 0 1 2 3 4

8. $\lvert 3 - (x - 1) \rvert \leq 8$

−4 −2 0 2 4 6 8 10 12

9. $\lvert 3r + 2 \rvert < -5$

−4 −3 −2 −1 0 1 2 3 4

For each graph, write an open sentence involving absolute value.

10.
−4 −3 −2 −1 0 1 2 3 4

11.
−4 −3 −2 −1 0 1 2 3 4

12.
−3 −2 −1 0 1 2 3 4 5

6-6 Study Guide and Intervention

Graphing Inequalities in Two Variables

Graph Linear Inequalities The solution set of an inequality that involves two variables is graphed by graphing a related linear equation that forms a boundary of a **half-plane**. The graph of the ordered pairs that make up the solution set of the inequality fill a region of the coordinate plane on one side of the half-plane.

Example Graph $y \leq -3x - 2$.

Graph $y = -3x - 2$.

Since $y \leq -3x - 2$ is the same as $y < -3x - 2$ and $y = -3x - 2$, the boundary is included in the solution set and the graph should be drawn as a solid line.

Select a point in each half plane and test it. Choose $(0, 0)$ and $(-2, -2)$.

$y \leq -3x - 2$ $y \leq -3x - 2$
$0 \leq -3(0) - 2$ $-2 \leq -3(-2) - 2$
$0 \leq -2$ is false. $-2 \leq 6 - 2$
                          $-2 \leq 4$ is true.

The half-plane that contains $(-2, -2)$ contains the solution. Shade that half-plane.

Exercises

Graph each inequality.

1. $y < 4$

2. $x \geq 1$

3. $3x \leq y$

4. $-x > y$

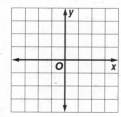

5. $x - y \geq 1$

6. $2x - 3y \leq 6$

7. $y < -\frac{1}{2}x - 3$

8. $4x - 3y < 6$

9. $3x + 6y \geq 12$

6-6 Study Guide and Intervention *(continued)*

Graphing Inequalities in Two Variables

Solve Real-World Problems When solving real-life inequalities, the domain and range of the inequality are often restricted to nonnegative numbers or to whole numbers.

Example BANKING A bank offers 4.5% annual interest on regular savings accounts and 6% annual interest on certificates of deposit (CD). If Marjean wants to earn at least $300 interest per year, how much money should she deposit in each type of account?

Let x = the amount deposited in a regular savings account.
Let y = the amount deposited in a CD.
Then $0.045x + 0.06y \geq 300$ is an open sentence representing this situation.

Solve for y in terms of x.

$0.045x + 0.06y \geq 300$ Original inequality
$\quad 0.06y \geq -0.045x + 300$ Subtract 0.045x from each side.
$\qquad y \geq -0.75x + 5000$ Divide each side by 0.06.

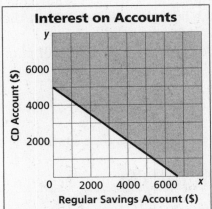

Graph $y \geq -0.75x + 5000$ and test the point $(0, 0)$.
Since $0 \geq -0.75(0) + 5000$ is false, shade the half-plane that does not contain $(0, 0)$.
One solution is $(4000, 2000)$. This represents $4000 deposited at 4.5% and $2,000 deposited at 6%.

Exercises

1. **SOCIAL EVENTS** Tickets for the school play cost $5 per student and $7 per adult. The school wants to earn at least $5,400 on each performance.

   a. Write an inequality that represents this situation.

   b. Graph the solution set.

   c. If 500 adult tickets are sold, what is the minimum number of student tickets that must be sold?

2. **MANUFACTURING** An auto parts company can produce 525 four-cylinder engines or 270 V-6 engines per day. It wants to produce up to 300,000 engines per year.

   a. Write an inequality that represents this situation.

   b. Are there restrictions on the domain or range?

3. **GEOMETRY** The perimeter of a rectangular lot is less than 800 feet. Write an inequality that represents the amount of fencing that will enclose the lot.

7-1 Study Guide and Intervention

Graphing Systems of Equations

Number of Solutions Two or more linear equations involving the same variables form a **system of equations**. A solution of the system of equations is an ordered pair of numbers that satisfies both equations. The table below summarizes information about systems of linear equations.

Graph of a System	intersecting lines	same line	parallel lines
Number of Solutions	exactly one solution	infinitely many solutions	no solution
Terminology	consistent and independent	consistent and dependent	inconsistent

Example Use the graph at the right to determine whether the system has *no* solution, *one* solution, or *infinitely many* solutions.

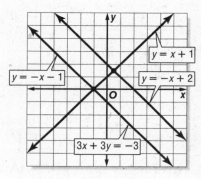

a. $y = -x + 2$
   $y = x + 1$

   Since the graphs of $y = -x + 2$ and $y = x + 1$ intersect, there is one solution.

b. $y = -x + 2$
   $3x + 3y = -3$

   Since the graphs of $y = -x + 2$ and $3x + 3y = -3$ are parallel, there are no solutions.

c. $3x + 3y = -3$
   $y = -x - 1$

   Since the graphs of $3x + 3y = -3$ and $y = -x - 1$ coincide, there are infinitely many solutions.

Exercises

Use the graph at the right to determine whether each system has *no* solution, *one* solution, or *infinitely many* solutions.

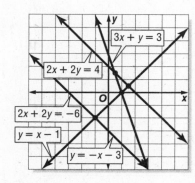

1. $y = -x - 3$
   $y = x - 1$

2. $2x + 2y = -6$
   $y = -x - 3$

3. $y = -x - 3$
   $2x + 2y = 4$

4. $2x + 2y = -6$
   $3x + y = 3$

7-1 Study Guide and Intervention (continued)

Graphing Systems of Equations

Solve by Graphing One method of solving a system of equations is to graph the equations on the same coordinate plane.

Example **Graph each system of equations. Then determine whether the system has *no* solution, *one* solution, or *infinitely many* solutions. If the system has one solution, name it.**

a. $x + y = 2$
$\quad x - y = 4$

The graphs intersect. Therefore, there is one solution. The point $(3, -1)$ seems to lie on both lines. Check this estimate by replacing x with 3 and y with -1 in each equation.

$\quad x + y = 2$
$3 + (-1) = 2$ ✓
$\quad x - y = 4$
$3 - (-1) = 3 + 1$ or 4 ✓

The solution is $(3, -1)$.

b. $y = 2x + 1$
$\quad 2y = 4x + 2$

The graphs coincide. Therefore there are infinitely many solutions.

Exercises

Graph each system of equations. Then determine whether the system has *no* solution, *one* solution, or *infinitely many* solutions. If the system has one solution, name it.

1. $y = -2$
$\quad 3x - y = -1$

2. $x = 2$
$\quad 2x + y = 1$

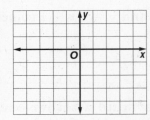

3. $y = \frac{1}{2}x$
$\quad x + y = 3$

4. $2x + y = 6$
$\quad 2x - y = -2$

5. $3x + 2y = 6$
$\quad 3x + 2y = -4$

6. $2y = -4x + 4$
$\quad y = -2x + 2$

7-2 Study Guide and Intervention

Substitution

Substitution One method of solving systems of equations is **substitution**.

Example 1 **Use substitution to solve the system of equations.**

$y = 2x$
$4x - y = -4$

Substitute $2x$ for y in the second equation.

$4x - y = -4$	Second equation
$4x - 2x = -4$	$y = 2x$
$2x = -4$	Combine like terms.
$\dfrac{2x}{2} = \dfrac{-4}{2}$	Divide each side by 2.
$x = -2$	Simplify.

Use $y = 2x$ to find the value of y.

$y = 2x$	First equation
$y = 2(-2)$	$x = -2$
$y = -4$	Simplify.

The solution is $(-2, -4)$.

Example 2 **Solve for one variable, then substitute.**

$x + 3y = 7$
$2x - 4y = -6$

Solve the first equation for x since the coefficient of x is 1.

$x + 3y = 7$	First equation
$x + 3y - 3y = 7 - 3y$	Subtract 3y from each side.
$x = 7 - 3y$	Simplify.

Find the value of y by substituting $7 - 3y$ for x in the second equation.

$2x - 4y = -6$	Second equation
$2(7 - 3y) - 4y = -6$	$x = 7 - 3y$
$14 - 6y - 4y = -6$	Distributive Property
$14 - 10y = -6$	Combine like terms.
$14 - 10y - 14 = -6 - 14$	Subtract 14 from each side.
$-10y = -20$	Simplify.
$\dfrac{-10y}{-10} = \dfrac{-20}{-10}$	Divide each side by −10.
$y = 2$	Simplify.

Use $y = 2$ to find the value of x.

$x = 7 - 3y$
$x = 7 - 3(2)$
$x = 1$

The solution is $(1, 2)$.

Exercises

Use substitution to solve each system of equations. If the system does *not* have exactly one solution, state whether it has *no* solution or *infinitely many* solutions.

1. $y = 4x$
$3x - y = 1$

2. $x = 2y$
$y = x - 2$

3. $x = 2y - 3$
$x = 2y + 4$

4. $x - 2y = -1$
$3y = x + 4$

5. $c - 4d = 1$
$2c - 8d = 2$

6. $x + 2y = 0$
$3x + 4y = 4$

7. $2b = 6a - 14$
$3a - b = 7$

8. $x + y = 16$
$2y = -2x + 2$

9. $y = -x + 3$
$2y + 2x = 4$

10. $x = 2y$
$0.25x + 0.5y = 10$

11. $x - 2y = -5$
$x + 2y = -1$

12. $-0.2x + y = 0.5$
$0.4x + y = 1.1$

Lesson 7-2

7-2 # Study Guide and Intervention *(continued)*

Substitution

Real-World Problems Substitution can also be used to solve real-world problems involving systems of equations. It may be helpful to use tables, charts, diagrams, or graphs to help you organize data.

Example **CHEMISTRY** How much of a 10% saline solution should be mixed with a 20% saline solution to obtain 1000 milliliters of a 12% saline solution?

Let s = the number of milliliters of 10% saline solution.
Let t = the number of milliliters of 20% saline solution.
Use a table to organize the information.

	10% saline	20% saline	12% saline
Total milliliters	s	t	1000
Milliliters of saline	0.10s	0.20t	0.12(1000)

Write a system of equations.
$s + t = 1000$
$0.10s + 0.20t = 0.12(1000)$
Use substitution to solve this system.

$s + t = 1000$	First equation
$s = 1000 - t$	Solve for s.
$0.10s + 0.20t = 0.12(1000)$	Second equation
$0.10(1000 - t) + 0.20t = 0.12(1000)$	$s = 1000 - t$
$100 - 0.10t + 0.20t = 0.12(1000)$	Distributive Property
$100 + 0.10t = 0.12(1000)$	Combine like terms.
$0.10t = 20$	Simplify.
$\dfrac{0.10t}{0.10} = \dfrac{20}{0.10}$	Divide each side by 0.10.
$t = 200$	Simplify.
$s + t = 1000$	First equation
$s + 200 = 1000$	$t = 200$
$s = 800$	Solve for s.

800 milliliters of 10% solution and 200 milliliters of 20% solution should be used.

Exercises

1. **SPORTS** At the end of the 2000-2001 football season, 31 Super Bowl games had been played with the current two football leagues, the American Football Conference (AFC) and the National Football Conference (NFC). The NFC won five more games than the AFC. How many games did each conference win? **Source:** *New York Times Almanac*

2. **CHEMISTRY** A lab needs to make 100 gallons of an 18% acid solution by mixing a 12% acid solution with a 20% solution. How many gallons of each solution are needed?

3. **GEOMETRY** The perimeter of a triangle is 24 inches. The longest side is 4 inches longer than the shortest side, and the shortest side is three-fourths the length of the middle side. Find the length of each side of the triangle.

7-3 Study Guide and Intervention

Elimination Using Addition and Subtraction

Elimination Using Addition In systems of equations in which the coefficients of the x or y terms are additive inverses, solve the system by adding the equations. Because one of the variables is eliminated, this method is called **elimination**.

Example 1 Use addition to solve the system of equations.

$x - 3y = 7$
$3x + 3y = 9$

Write the equations in column form and add to eliminate y.

$$\begin{array}{r} x - 3y = 7 \\ (+)\ 3x + 3y = 9 \\ \hline 4x \quad\quad = 16 \end{array}$$

Solve for x.

$$\frac{4x}{4} = \frac{16}{4}$$
$$x = 4$$

Substitute 4 for x in either equation and solve for y.

$$4 - 3y = 7$$
$$4 - 3y - 4 = 7 - 4$$
$$-3y = 3$$
$$\frac{-3y}{-3} = \frac{3}{-3}$$
$$y = -1$$

The solution is $(4, -1)$.

Example 2 The sum of two numbers is 70 and their difference is 24. Find the numbers.

Let x represent one number and y represent the other number.

$$\begin{array}{r} x + y = 70 \\ (+)\ x - y = 24 \\ \hline 2x \quad\quad = 94 \end{array}$$
$$\frac{2x}{2} = \frac{94}{2}$$
$$x = 47$$

Substitute 47 for x in either equation.

$$47 + y = 70$$
$$47 + y - 47 = 70 - 47$$
$$y = 23$$

The numbers are 47 and 23.

Exercises

Use elimination to solve each system of equations.

1. $x + y = -4$
    $x - y = 2$

2. $2m - 3n = 14$
    $m + 3n = -11$

3. $3a - b = -9$
    $-3a - 2b = 0$

4. $-3x - 4y = -1$
    $3x - y = -4$

5. $3c + d = 4$
    $2c - d = 6$

6. $-2x + 2y = 9$
    $2x - y = -6$

7. $2x + 2y = -2$
    $3x - 2y = 12$

8. $4x - 2y = -1$
    $-4x + 4y = -2$

9. $x - y = 2$
    $x + y = -3$

10. $2x - 3y = 12$
    $4x + 3y = 24$

11. $-0.2x + y = 0.5$
    $0.2x + 2y = 1.6$

12. $0.1x + 0.3y = 0.9$
    $0.1x - 0.3y = 0.2$

13. Rema is older than Ken. The difference of their ages is 12 and the sum of their ages is 50. Find the age of each.

14. The sum of the digits of a two-digit number is 12. The difference of the digits is 2. Find the number if the units digit is larger than the tens digit.

Lesson 7-3

7-3 Study Guide and Intervention (continued)

Elimination Using Addition and Subtraction

Elimination Using Subtraction In systems of equations where the coefficients of the x or y terms are the same, solve the system by subtracting the equations.

Example Use subtraction to solve the system of equations.

$2x - 3y = 11$
$5x - 3y = 14$

$$\begin{array}{rl} 2x - 3y = & 11 \\ (-)\ 5x - 3y = & 14 \\ \hline -3x\ \ \ \ \ \ = & -3 \end{array}$$ Write the equations in column form and subtract.

Subtract the two equations. y is eliminated.

$$\dfrac{-3x}{-3} = \dfrac{-3}{-3}$$ Divide each side by -3.

$$x = 1$$ Simplify.

$$2(1) - 3y = 11$$ Substitute 1 for x in either equation.
$$2 - 3y = 11$$ Simplify.
$$2 - 3y - 2 = 11 - 2$$ Subtract 2 from each side.
$$-3y = 9$$ Simplify.
$$\dfrac{-3y}{-3} = \dfrac{9}{-3}$$ Divide each side by -3.
$$y = -3$$ Simplify.

The solution is $(1, -3)$.

Exercises

Use elimination to solve each system of equations.

1. $6x + 5y = 4$
$\ \ \ \ \ 6x - 7y = -20$

2. $3m - 4n = -14$
$\ \ \ \ \ 3m + 2n = -2$

3. $3a + b = 1$
$\ \ \ \ \ a + b = 3$

4. $-3x - 4y = -23$
$\ \ \ \ \ -3x + y = 2$

5. $c - 3d = 11$
$\ \ \ \ \ 2c - 3d = 16$

6. $x - 2y = 6$
$\ \ \ \ \ x + y = 3$

7. $2a - 3b = -13$
$\ \ \ \ \ 2a + 2b = 7$

8. $4x + 2y = 6$
$\ \ \ \ \ 4x + 4y = 10$

9. $5s - t = 6$
$\ \ \ \ \ 5s + 2t = 3$

10. $6x - 3y = 12$
$\ \ \ \ \ \ 4x - 3y = 24$

11. $x + 2y = 3.5$
$\ \ \ \ \ \ x - 3y = -9$

12. $0.2x + y = 0.7$
$\ \ \ \ \ \ 0.2x + 2y = 1.2$

13. The sum of two numbers is 70. One number is ten more than twice the other number. Find the numbers.

14. GEOMETRY Two angles are supplementary. The measure of one angle is 10° more than three times the other. Find the measure of each angle.

7-4

Study Guide and Intervention

Elimination Using Multiplication

Elimination Using Multiplication Some systems of equations cannot be solved simply by adding or subtracting the equations. In such cases, one or both equations must first be multiplied by a number before the system can be solved by elimination.

Example 1 Use elimination to solve the system of equations.

$x + 10y = 3$
$4x + 5y = 5$

If you multiply the second equation by -2, you can eliminate the y terms.

$$\begin{aligned} x + 10y &= 3 \\ (+)\ -8x - 10y &= -10 \\ \hline -7x &= -7 \end{aligned}$$

$$\frac{-7x}{-7} = \frac{-7}{-7}$$

$$x = 1$$

Substitute 1 for x in either equation.

$$1 + 10y = 3$$
$$1 + 10y - 1 = 3 - 1$$
$$10y = 2$$
$$\frac{10y}{10} = \frac{2}{10}$$
$$y = \frac{1}{5}$$

The solution is $\left(1, \frac{1}{5}\right)$.

Example 2 Use elimination to solve the system of equations.

$3x - 2y = -7$
$2x - 5y = 10$

If you multiply the first equation by 2 and the second equation by -3, you can eliminate the x terms.

$$\begin{aligned} 6x - 4y &= -14 \\ (+)\ -6x + 15y &= -30 \\ \hline 11y &= -44 \end{aligned}$$

$$\frac{11y}{11} = \frac{-44}{11}$$

$$y = -4$$

Substitute -4 for y in either equation.

$$3x - 2(-4) = -7$$
$$3x + 8 = -7$$
$$3x + 8 - 8 = -7 - 8$$
$$3x = -15$$
$$\frac{3x}{3} = \frac{-15}{3}$$
$$x = -5$$

The solution is $(-5, -4)$.

Exercises

Use elimination to solve each system of equations.

1. $2x + 3y = 6$
   $x + 2y = 5$

2. $2m + 3n = 4$
   $-m + 2n = 5$

3. $3a - b = 2$
   $a + 2b = 3$

4. $4x + 5y = 6$
   $6x - 7y = -20$

5. $4c - 3d = 22$
   $2c - d = 10$

6. $3x - 4y = -4$
   $x + 3y = -10$

7. $4s - t = 9$
   $5s + 2t = 8$

8. $4a - 3b = -8$
   $2a + 2b = 3$

9. $2x + 2y = 5$
   $4x - 4y = 10$

10. $6x - 4y = -8$
    $4x + 2y = -3$

11. $4x + 2y = -5$
    $-2x - 4y = 1$

12. $2x + y = 3.5$
    $-x + 2y = 2.5$

13. **GARDENING** The length of Sally's garden is 4 meters greater than 3 times the width. The perimeter of her garden is 72 meters. What are the dimensions of Sally's garden?

14. Anita is $4\frac{1}{2}$ years older than Basilio. Three times Anita's age added to six times Basilio's age is 36. How old are Anita and Basilio?

Lesson 7-4

7-4 Study Guide and Intervention (continued)

Elimination Using Multiplication

Determine the Best Method The methods to use for solving systems of linear equations are summarized in the table below.

Method	The Best Time to Use
Graphing	to estimate the solution, since graphing usually does not give an exact solution
Substitution	if one of the variables in either equation has a coefficient of 1 or -1
Elimination Using Addition	if one of the variables has opposite coefficients in the two equations
Elimination Using Subtraction	if one of the variables has the same coefficient in the two equations
Elimination Using Multiplication	if none of the coefficients are 1 or -1 and neither of the variables can be eliminated by simply adding or subtracting the equations

Example Determine the best method to solve the system of equations. Then solve the system.

$6x + 2y = 20$
$-2x + 4y = -16$

Since the coefficients of x will be additive inverses of each other if you multiply the second equation by 3, use elimination.

$$6x + 2y = 20$$
$$(+) -6x + 12y = -48 \quad \text{Multiply the second equation by 3.}$$
$$14y = -28 \quad \text{Add the two equations. } x \text{ is eliminated.}$$
$$\frac{14y}{14} = \frac{-28}{14} \quad \text{Divide each side by 14.}$$
$$y = -2 \quad \text{Simplify.}$$

$$6x + 2(-2) = 20 \quad \text{Substitute } -2 \text{ for } y \text{ in either equation.}$$
$$6x - 4 = 20 \quad \text{Simplify.}$$
$$6x - 4 + 4 = 20 + 4 \quad \text{Add 4 to each side.}$$
$$6x = 24 \quad \text{Simplify.}$$
$$\frac{6x}{6} = \frac{24}{6} \quad \text{Divide each side by 6.}$$
$$x = 4 \quad \text{Simplify.}$$

The solution is $(4, -2)$.

Exercises

Determine the best method to solve each system of equations. Then solve the system.

1. $x + 2y = 3$
   $x + y = 1$

2. $m + 6n = -8$
   $m = 2n + 8$

3. $a - b = 6$
   $a = 2b + 7$

4. $4x + y = 15$
   $-x - 3y = -12$

5. $3c - d = 14$
   $c - d = 2$

6. $x + 2y = -9$
   $y = 4x$

7. $4x = 2y - 10$
   $x + 2y = 5$

8. $x = -2y$
   $4x + 4y = -10$

9. $2s - 3t = 42$
   $3s + 2t = 24$

10. $4a - 4b = -10$
    $2a + 4b = -2$

11. $4x + 10y = -6$
    $-2x - 10y = 2$

12. $2x = y - 3$
    $-x + y = 0$

7-5 # Study Guide and Intervention

Graphing Systems of Inequalities

Systems of Inequalities The solution of a **system of inequalities** is the set of all ordered pairs that satisfy both inequalities. If you graph the inequalities in the same coordinate plane, the solution is the region where the graphs overlap.

Example 1 **Solve the system of inequalities by graphing.**
$y > x + 2$
$y \le -2x - 1$

The solution includes the ordered pairs in the intersection of the graphs. This region is shaded at the right. The graphs of $y = x + 2$ and $y = -2x - 1$ are boundaries of this region. The graph of $y = x + 2$ is dashed and is not included in the graph of $y > x + 2$.

Example 2 **Solve the system of inequalities by graphing.**
$x + y > 4$
$x + y < -1$

The graphs of $x + y = 4$ and $x + y = -1$ are parallel. Because the two regions have no points in common, the system of inequalities has no solution.

Exercises

Solve each system of inequalities by graphing.

1. $y > -1$
   $x < 0$

2. $y > -2x + 2$
   $y \le x + 1$

3. $y < x + 1$
   $3x + 4y \ge 12$

4. $2x + y \ge 1$
   $x - y \ge -2$

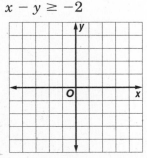

5. $y \le 2x + 3$
   $y \ge -1 + 2x$

6. $5x - 2y < 6$
   $y > -x + 1$

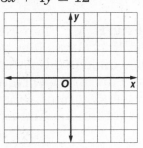

Lesson 7-5

7-5 Study Guide and Intervention *(continued)*

Graphing Systems of Inequalities

Real-World Problems In real-world problems, sometimes only whole numbers make sense for the solution, and often only positive values of x and y make sense.

Example **BUSINESS** AAA Gem Company produces necklaces and bracelets. In a 40-hour week, the company has 400 gems to use. A necklace requires 40 gems and a bracelet requires 10 gems. It takes 2 hours to produce a necklace and a bracelet requires one hour. How many of each type can be produced in a week?

Let n = the number of necklaces that will be produced and b = the number of bracelets that will be produced. Neither n or b can be a negative number, so the following system of inequalities represents the conditions of the problems.

$n \geq 0$

$b \geq 0$

$b + 2n \leq 40$

$10b + 40n \leq 400$

The solution is the set ordered pairs in the intersection of the graphs. This region is shaded at the right. Only whole-number solutions, such as (5, 20) make sense in this problem.

Exercises

For each exercise, graph the solution set. List three possible solutions to the problem.

1. **HEALTH** Mr. Flowers is on a restricted diet that allows him to have between 1600 and 2000 Calories per day. His daily fat intake is restricted to between 45 and 55 grams. What daily Calorie and fat intakes are acceptable?

2. **RECREATION** Maria had $150 in gift certificates to use at a record store. She bought fewer than 20 recordings. Each tape cost $5.95 and each CD cost $8.95. How many of each type of recording might she have bought?

8-1 Study Guide and Intervention

Multiplying Monomials

Multiply Monomials A **monomial** is a number, a variable, or a product of a number and one or more variables. An expression of the form x^n is called a **power** and represents the product you obtain when x is used as a factor n times. To multiply two powers that have the same base, add the exponents.

Product of Powers	For any number a and all integers m and n, $a^m \cdot a^n = a^{m+n}$.

Example 1 Simplify $(3x^6)(5x^2)$.

$$(3x^6)(5x^2) = (3)(5)(x^6 \cdot x^2) \quad \text{Associative Property}$$
$$= (3 \cdot 5)(x^{6+2}) \quad \text{Product of Powers}$$
$$= 15x^8 \quad \text{Simplify.}$$

The product is $15x^8$.

Example 2 Simplify $(-4a^3b)(3a^2b^5)$.

$$(-4a^3b)(3a^2b^5) = (-4)(3)(a^3 \cdot a^2)(b \cdot b^5)$$
$$= -12(a^{3+2})(b^{1+5})$$
$$= -12a^5b^6$$

The product is $-12a^5b^6$.

Exercises

Simplify.

1. $y(y^5)$

2. $n^2 \cdot n^7$

3. $(-7x^2)(x^4)$

4. $x(x^2)(x^4)$

5. $m \cdot m^5$

6. $(-x^3)(-x^4)$

7. $(2a^2)(8a)$

8. $(rs)(rs^3)(s^2)$

9. $(x^2y)(4xy^3)$

10. $\frac{1}{3}(2a^3b)(6b^3)$

11. $(-4x^3)(-5x^7)$

12. $(-3j^2k^4)(2jk^6)$

13. $(5a^2bc^3)\left(\frac{1}{5}abc^4\right)$

14. $(-5xy)(4x^2)(y^4)$

15. $(10x^3yz^2)(-2xy^5z)$

8-1 Study Guide and Intervention (continued)

Multiplying Monomials

Powers of Monomials An expression of the form $(x^m)^n$ is called a **power of a power** and represents the product you obtain when x^m is used as a factor n times. To find the power of a power, multiply exponents.

Power of a Power	For any number a and all integers m and n, $(a^m)^n = a^{mn}$.
Power of a Product	For any number a and all integers m and n, $(ab)^m = a^m b^m$.

Example Simplify $(-2ab^2)^3(a^2)^4$.

$$
\begin{aligned}
(-2ab^2)^3(a^2)^4 &= (-2ab^2)^3(a^8) && \text{Power of a Power} \\
&= (-2)^3(a^3)(b^2)^3(a^8) && \text{Power of a Product} \\
&= (-2)^3(a^3)(a^8)(b^2)^3 && \text{Commutative Property} \\
&= (-2)^3(a^{11})(b^2)^3 && \text{Product of Powers} \\
&= -8a^{11}b^6 && \text{Power of a Power}
\end{aligned}
$$

The product is $-8a^{11}b^6$.

Exercises

Simplify.

1. $(y^5)^2$

2. $(n^7)^4$

3. $(x^2)^5(x^3)$

4. $-3(ab^4)^3$

5. $(-3ab^4)^3$

6. $(4x^2b)^3$

7. $(4a^2)^2(b^3)$

8. $(4x)^2(b^3)$

9. $(x^2y^4)^5$

10. $(2a^3b^2)(b^3)^2$

11. $(-4xy)^3(-2x^2)^3$

12. $(-3j^2k^3)^2(2j^2k)^3$

13. $(25a^2b)^3\left(\dfrac{1}{5}abc\right)^2$

14. $(2xy)^2(-3x^2)(4y^4)$

15. $(2x^3y^2z^2)^3(x^2z)^4$

16. $(-2n^6y^5)(-6n^3y^2)(ny)^3$

17. $(-3a^3n^4)(-3a^3n)^4$

18. $-3(2x)^4(4x^5y)^2$

8-2 Study Guide and Intervention

Dlividing Monomials

Quotients of Monomials To divide two powers with the same base, subtract the exponents.

Quotient of Powers	For all integers m and n and any nonzero number a, $\dfrac{a^m}{a^n} = a^{m-n}$.
Power of a Quotient	For any integer m and any real numbers a and b, $b \neq 0$, $\left(\dfrac{a}{b}\right)^m = \dfrac{a^m}{b^m}$.

Example 1 Simplify $\dfrac{a^4 b^7}{ab^2}$. Assume neither a nor b is equal to zero.

$$\dfrac{a^4 b^7}{ab^2} = \left(\dfrac{a^4}{a}\right)\left(\dfrac{b^7}{b^2}\right) \qquad \text{Group powers with the same base.}$$

$$= (a^{4-1})(b^{7-2}) \qquad \text{Quotient of Powers}$$

$$= a^3 b^5 \qquad \text{Simplify.}$$

The quotient is $a^3 b^5$.

Example 2 Simplify $\left(\dfrac{2a^3 b^5}{3b^2}\right)^3$. Assume that b is not equal to zero.

$$\left(\dfrac{2a^3 b^5}{3b^2}\right)^3 = \dfrac{(2a^3 b^5)^3}{(3b^2)^3} \qquad \text{Power of a Quotient}$$

$$= \dfrac{2^3 (a^3)^3 (b^5)^3}{(3)^3 (b^2)^3} \qquad \text{Power of a Product}$$

$$= \dfrac{8a^9 b^{15}}{27 b^6} \qquad \text{Power of a Power}$$

$$= \dfrac{8a^9 b^9}{27} \qquad \text{Quotient of Powers}$$

The quotient is $\dfrac{8a^9 b^9}{27}$.

Exercises

Simplify. Assume that no denominator is equal to zero.

1. $\dfrac{5^5}{5^2}$

2. $\dfrac{m^6}{m^4}$

3. $\dfrac{p^5 n^4}{p^2 n}$

4. $\dfrac{a^2}{a}$

5. $\dfrac{x^5 y^3}{x^5 y^2}$

6. $\dfrac{-2y^7}{14 y^5}$

7. $\dfrac{xy^6}{y^4 x}$

8. $\left(\dfrac{2a^2 b}{a}\right)^3$

9. $\left(\dfrac{4p^4 q^4}{3p^2 q^2}\right)^3$

10. $\left(\dfrac{2v^5 w^3}{v^4 w^3}\right)^4$

11. $\left(\dfrac{3r^6 s^3}{2r^5 s}\right)^4$

12. $\dfrac{r^7 s^7 t^2}{s^3 r^3 t^2}$

Lesson 8-2

8-2 Study Guide and Intervention (continued)

Dividing Monomials

Negative Exponents Any nonzero number raised to the zero power is 1; for example, $(-0.5)^0 = 1$. Any nonzero number raised to a negative power is equal to the reciprocal of the number raised to the opposite power; for example, $6^{-3} = \frac{1}{6^3}$. These definitions can be used to simplify expressions that have negative exponents.

Zero Exponent	For any nonzero number a, $a^0 = 1$.
Negative Exponent Property	For any nonzero number a and any integer n, $a^{-n} = \frac{1}{a^n}$ and $\frac{1}{a^{-n}} = a^n$.

The simplified form of an expression containing negative exponents must contain only positive exponents.

Example Simplify $\frac{4a^{-3}b^6}{16a^2b^6c^{-5}}$. **Assume that the denominator is not equal to zero.**

$\frac{4a^{-3}b^6}{16a^2b^6c^{-5}} = \left(\frac{4}{16}\right)\left(\frac{a^{-3}}{a^2}\right)\left(\frac{b^6}{b^6}\right)\left(\frac{1}{c^{-5}}\right)$ Group powers with the same base.

$\qquad = \frac{1}{4}(a^{-3-2})(b^{6-6})(c^5)$ Quotient of Powers and Negative Exponent Properties

$\qquad = \frac{1}{4}a^{-5}b^0c^5$ Simplify.

$\qquad = \frac{1}{4}\left(\frac{1}{a^5}\right)(1)c^5$ Negative Exponent and Zero Exponent Properties

$\qquad = \frac{c^5}{4a^5}$ Simplify.

The solution is $\frac{c^5}{4a^5}$.

Exercises

Simplify. Assume that no denominator is equal to zero.

1. $\frac{2^2}{2^{-3}}$

2. $\frac{m}{m^{-4}}$

3. $\frac{p^{-8}}{p^3}$

4. $\frac{b^{-4}}{b^{-5}}$

5. $\frac{(-x^{-1}y)^0}{4w^{-1}y^2}$

6. $\frac{(a^2b^3)^2}{(ab)^{-2}}$

7. $\frac{x^4y^0}{x^{-2}}$

8. $\frac{(6a^{-1}b)^2}{(b^2)^4}$

9. $\frac{(3st)^2u^{-4}}{s^{-1}t^2u^7}$

10. $\frac{s^{-3}t^{-5}}{(s^2t^3)^{-1}}$

11. $\left(\frac{4m^2n^2}{8m^{-1}\ell}\right)^0$

12. $\frac{(-2mn^2)^{-3}}{4m^{-6}n^4}$

8-3 **Study Guide and Intervention**

Scientific Notation

Scientific Notation Keeping track of place value in very large or very small numbers written in standard form may be difficult. It is more efficient to write such numbers in scientific notation. A number is expressed in scientific notation when it is written as a product of two factors, one factor that is greater than or equal to 1 and less than 10 and one factor that is a power of ten.

Scientific Notation	A number is in scientific notation when it is in the form $a \times 10^n$, where $1 \le a < 10$ and n is an integer.

Example 1 **Express 3.52×10^4 in standard notation.**

$3.52 \times 10^4 = 3.52 \times 10,000$
$= 35,200$

The decimal point moved 4 places to the right.

Example 2 **Express 6.21×10^{-5} in standard notation.**

$6.21 \times 10^{-5} = 6.21 \times \dfrac{1}{10^5}$
$= 6.21 \times 0.00001$
$= 0.0000621$

The decimal point moved 5 places to the left.

Example 3 **Express 37,600,000 in scientific notation.**

$37,600,000 = 3.76 \times 10^7$

The decimal point moved 7 places so that it is between the 3 and the 7. Since $37,600,000 > 1$, the exponent is positive.

Example 4 **Express 0.0000549 in scientific notation.**

$0.0000549 = 5.49 \times 10^{-5}$

The decimal point moved 5 places so that it is between the 5 and the 4. Since $0.0000549 < 1$, the exponent is negative.

Exercises

Express each number in standard notation.

1. 3.65×10^5 **2.** 7.02×10^{-4} **3.** 8.003×10^8

4. 7.451×10^6 **5.** 5.91×10^0 **6.** 7.99×10^{-1}

7. 8.9354×10^{10} **8.** 8.1×10^{-9} **9.** 4×10^{15}

Express each number in scientific notation.

10. 0.0000456   **11.** 0.00001   **12.** 590,000,000

13. 0.00000000012   **14.** 0.000080436   **15.** 0.03621

16. 433×10^4 **17.** 0.0042×10^{-3} **18.** 50,000,000,000

Lesson 8-3

8-3 Study Guide and Intervention (continued)

Scientific Notation

Products and Quotients with Scientific Notation You can use properties of powers to compute with numbers written in scientific notation.

Example 1 Evaluate $(6.7 \times 10^3)(2 \times 10^{-5})$. Express the result in scientific and standard notation.

$$
\begin{aligned}
(6.7 \times 10^3)(2 \times 10^{-5}) &= (6.7 \times 2)(10^3 \times 10^{-5}) && \text{Associative Property}\\
&= 13.4 \times 10^{-2} && \text{Product of Powers}\\
&= (1.34 \times 10^1) \times 10^{-2} && 13.4 = 1.34 \times 10^1\\
&= 1.34 \times (10^1 \times 10^{-2}) && \text{Associative Property}\\
&= 1.34 \times 10^{-1} \text{ or } 0.134 && \text{Product of Powers}
\end{aligned}
$$

The solution is 1.34×10^{-1} or 0.134.

Example 2 Evaluate $\dfrac{1.5088 \times 10^8}{4.1 \times 10^5}$. Express the result in scientific and standard notation.

$$
\begin{aligned}
\frac{1.5088 \times 10^8}{4.1 \times 10^5} &= \left(\frac{1.5088}{4.1}\right)\left(\frac{10^8}{10^5}\right) && \text{Associative Property}\\
&= 0.368 \times 10^3 && \text{Quotient of Powers}\\
&= (3.68 \times 10^{-1}) \times 10^3 && 0.368 = 3.68 \times 10^{-1}\\
&= 3.68 \times (10^{-1} \times 10^3) && \text{Associative Property}\\
&= 3.68 \times 10^2 \text{ or } 368 && \text{Product of Powers}
\end{aligned}
$$

The solution is 3.68×10^2 or 368.

Exercises

Evaluate. Express each result in scientific and standard notation.

1. $\dfrac{1.4 \times 10^4}{2 \times 10^2}$

2. $\dfrac{3 \times 10^{-12}}{2 \times 10^{-15}}$

3. $(3.2 \times 10^{-2})(2.0 \times 10^2)$

4. $\dfrac{1.2672 \times 10^{-8}}{2.4 \times 10^{-12}}$

5. $(7.7 \times 10^5)(2.1 \times 10^2)$

6. $\dfrac{9.72 \times 10^8}{7.2 \times 10^{10}}$

7. $(3.3 \times 10^5)(1.5 \times 10^{-4})$

8. $\dfrac{3.3 \times 10^{-12}}{1.1 \times 10^{-14}}$

9. $\dfrac{4 \times 10^{-4}}{2.5 \times 10^2}$

10. **FUEL CONSUMPTION** North America burned 4.5×10^{16} BTU of petroleum in 1998. At this rate, how many BTU's will be burned in 9 years? **Source:** *The New York Times 2001 Almanac*

11. **OIL PRODUCTION** If the United States produced 6.25×10^9 barrels of crude oil in 1998, and Canada produced 1.98×10^9 barrels, what is the quotient of their production rates? Write a statement using this quotient. **Source:** *The New York Times 2001 Almanac*

8-4 Study Guide and Intervention

Polynomials

Degree of a Polynomial A **polynomial** is a monomial or a sum of monomials. A **binomial** is the sum of two monomials, and a **trinomial** is the sum of three monomials. Polynomials with more than three terms have no special name. The **degree** of a monomial is the sum of the exponents of all its variables. The **degree of the polynomial** is the same as the degree of the monomial term with the highest degree.

Example State whether each expression is a polynomial. If the expression is a polynomial, identify it as a *monomial*, *binomial*, or *trinomial*. Then give the degree of the polynomial.

Expression	Polynomial?	Monomial, Binomial, or Trinomial?	Degree of the Polynomial
$3x - 7xyz$	Yes. $3x - 7xyz = 3x + (-7xyz)$, which is the sum of two monomials	binomial	3
-25	Yes. -25 is a real number.	monomial	0
$7n^3 + 3n^{-4}$	No. $3n^{-4} = \dfrac{3}{n^4}$, which is not a monomial	none of these	—
$9x^3 + 4x + x + 4 + 2x$	Yes. The expression simplifies to $9x^3 + 7x + 4$, which is the sum of three monomials	trinomial	3

Exercises

State whether each expression is a polynomial. If the expression is a polynomial, identify it as a *monomial*, *binomial*, or *trinomial*.

1. 36

2. $\dfrac{3}{q^2} + 5$

3. $7x - x + 5$

4. $8g^2h - 7gh + 2$

5. $\dfrac{1}{4y^2} + 5y - 8$

6. $6x + x^2$

Find the degree of each polynomial.

7. $4x^2y^3z$

8. $-2abc$

9. $15m$

10. $s + 5t$

11. 22

12. $18x^2 + 4yz - 10y$

13. $x^4 - 6x^2 - 2x^3 - 10$

14. $2x^3y^2 - 4xy^3$

15. $-2r^8s^4 + 7r^2s - 4r^7s^6$

16. $9x^2 + yz^8$

17. $8b + bc^5$

18. $4x^4y - 8zx^2 + 2x^5$

19. $4x^2 - 1$

20. $9abc + bc - d^5$

21. $h^3m + 6h^4m^2 - 7$

Lesson 8-4

8-4 # Study Guide and Intervention *(continued)*

Polynomials

Write Polynomials in Order The terms of a polynomial are usually arranged so that the powers of one variable are in **ascending** (increasing) order or **descending** (decreasing) order.

Example 1 Arrange the terms of each polynomial so that the powers of x are in ascending order.

a. $x^4 - x^2 + 5x^3$
   $-x^2 + 5x^3 + x^4$

b. $8x^3y - y^2 + 6x^2y + xy^2$
   $-y^2 + xy^2 + 6x^2y + 8x^3y$

Example 2 Arrange the terms of each polynomial so that the powers of x are in descending order.

a. $x^4 + 4x^5 - x^2$
   $4x^5 + x^4 - x^2$

b. $-6xy + y^3 - x^2y^2 + x^4y^2$
   $x^4y^2 - x^2y^2 - 6xy + y^3$

Exercises

Arrange the terms of each polynomial so that the powers of x are in ascending order.

1. $5x + x^2 + 6$

2. $6x + 9 - 4x^2$

3. $4xy + 2y + 6x^2$

4. $6y^2x - 6x^2y + 2$

5. $x^4 + x^3 + x^2$

6. $2x^3 - x + 3x^7$

7. $-5cx + 10c^2x^3 + 15cx^2$

8. $-4nx - 5n^3x^3 + 5$

9. $4xy + 2y + 5x^2$

Arrange the terms of each polynomial so that the powers of x are in descending order.

10. $2x + x^2 - 5$

11. $20x - 10x^2 + 5x^3$

12. $x^2 + 4yx - 10x^5$

13. $9bx + 3bx^2 - 6x^3$

14. $x^3 + x^5 - x^2$

15. $ax^2 + 8a^2x^5 - 4$

16. $3x^3y - 4xy^2 - x^4y^2 + y^5$

17. $x^4 + 4x^3 - 7x^5 + 1$

18. $-3x^6 - x^5 + 2x^8$

19. $-15cx^2 + 8c^2x^5 + cx$

20. $24x^2y - 12x^3y^2 + 6x^4$

21. $-15x^3 + 10x^4y^2 + 7xy^2$

8-5 Study Guide and Intervention

Adding and Subtracting Polynomials

Add Polynomials To add polynomials, you can group like terms horizontally or write them in column form, aligning like terms vertically. **Like terms** are monomial terms that are either identical or differ only in their coefficients, such as $3p$ and $-5p$ or $2x^2y$ and $8x^2y$.

Example 1 Find $(2x^2 + x - 8) + (3x - 4x^2 + 2)$.

Horizontal Method
Group like terms.

$(2x^2 + x - 8) + (3x - 4x^2 + 2)$
$= [(2x^2 + (-4x^2)] + (x + 3x) + [(-8) + 2)]$
$= -2x^2 + 4x - 6.$

The sum is $-2x^2 + 4x - 6$.

Example 2 Find $(3x^2 + 5xy) + (xy + 2x^2)$.

Vertical Method
Align like terms in columns and add.

$$3x^2 + 5xy$$
$$\underline{(+)\ 2x^2 +\ \ xy}\quad \text{Put the terms in descending order.}$$
$$5x^2 + 6xy$$

The sum is $5x^2 + 6xy$.

Exercises

Find each sum.

1. $(4a - 5) + (3a + 6)$

2. $(6x + 9) + (4x^2 - 7)$

3. $(6xy + 2y + 6x) + (4xy - x)$

4. $(x^2 + y^2) + (-x^2 + y^2)$

5. $(3p^2 - 2p + 3) + (p^2 - 7p + 7)$

6. $(2x^2 + 5xy + 4y^2) + (-xy - 6x^2 + 2y^2)$

7. $(5p + 2q) + (2p^2 - 8q + 1)$

8. $(4x^2 - x + 4) + (5x + 2x^2 + 2)$

9. $(6x^2 + 3x) + (x^2 - 4x - 3)$

10. $(x^2 + 2xy + y^2) + (x^2 - xy - 2y^2)$

11. $(2a - 4b - c) + (-2a - b - 4c)$

12. $(6xy^2 + 4xy) + (2xy - 10xy^2 + y^2)$

13. $(2p - 5q) + (3p + 6q) + (p - q)$

14. $(2x^2 - 6) + (5x^2 + 2) + (-x^2 - 7)$

15. $(3z^2 + 5z) + (z^2 + 2z) + (z - 4)$

16. $(8x^2 + 4x + 3y^2 + y) + (6x^2 - x + 4y)$

Lesson 8-5

8-5 Study Guide and Intervention *(continued)*

Adding and Subtracting Polynomials

Subtract Polynomials You can subtract a polynomial by adding its additive inverse. To find the additive inverse of a polynomial, replace each term with its additive inverse or opposite.

Example Find $(3x^2 + 2x - 6) - (2x + x^2 + 3)$.

Horizontal Method

Use additive inverses to rewrite as addition. Then group like terms.

$(3x^2 + 2x - 6) - (2x + x^2 + 3)$
$= (3x^2 + 2x - 6) + [(-2x) + (-x^2) + (-3)]$
$= [3x^2 + (-x^2)] + [2x + (-2x)] + [-6 + (-3)]$
$= 2x^2 + (-9)$
$= 2x^2 - 9$

The difference is $2x^2 - 9$.

Vertical Method

Align like terms in columns and subtract by adding the additive inverse.

$$\begin{array}{r} 3x^2 + 2x - 6 \\ (-)\ \underline{x^2 + 2x + 3} \end{array}$$

$$\begin{array}{r} 3x^2 + 2x - 6 \\ (+)\ \underline{-x^2 - 2x - 3} \\ 2x^2 \qquad\ - 9 \end{array}$$

The difference is $2x^2 - 9$.

Exercises

Find each difference.

1. $(3a - 5) - (5a + 1)$

2. $(9x + 2) - (-3x^2 - 5)$

3. $(9xy + y - 2x) - (6xy - 2x)$

4. $(x^2 + y^2) - (-x^2 + y^2)$

5. $(6p^2 + 4p + 5) - (2p^2 - 5p + 1)$

6. $(6x^2 + 5xy - 2y^2) - (-xy - 2x^2 - 4y^2)$

7. $(8p - 5q) - (-6p^2 + 6q - 3)$

8. $(8x^2 - 4x - 3) - (-2x - x^2 + 5)$

9. $(3x^2 - 2x) - (3x^2 + 5x - 1)$

10. $(4x^2 + 6xy + 2y^2) - (-x^2 + 2xy - 5y^2)$

11. $(2h - 6j - 2k) - (-7h - 5j - 4k)$

12. $(9xy^2 + 5xy) - (-2xy - 8xy^2)$

13. $(2a - 8b) - (-3a + 5b)$

14. $(2x^2 - 8) - (-2x^2 - 6)$

15. $(6z^2 + 4z + 2) - (4z^2 + z)$

16. $(6x^2 - 5x + 1) - (-7x^2 - 2x + 4)$

8-6 Study Guide and Intervention

Multiplying a Polynomial by a Monomial

Product of Monomial and Polynomial The Distributive Property can be used to multiply a polynomial by a monomial. You can multiply horizontally or vertically. Sometimes multiplying results in like terms. The products can be simplified by combining like terms.

Example 1 Find $-3x^2(4x^2 + 6x - 8)$.

Horizontal Method

$-3x^2(4x^2 + 6x - 8)$
$= -3x^2(4x^2) + (-3x^2)(6x) - (-3x^2)(8)$
$= -12x^4 + (-18x^3) - (-24x^2)$
$= -12x^4 - 18x^3 + 24x^2$

Vertical Method

$$\begin{array}{r} 4x^2 + 6x - 8 \\ (\times) \qquad\qquad -3x^2 \\ \hline -12x^4 - 18x^3 + 24x^2 \end{array}$$

The product is $-12x^4 - 18x^3 + 24x^2$.

Example 2 Simplify $-2(4x^2 + 5x) - x(x^2 + 6x)$.

$-2(4x^2 + 5x) - x(x^2 + 6x)$
$= -2(4x^2) + (-2)(5x) + (-x)(x^2) + (-x)(6x)$
$= -8x^2 + (-10x) + (-x^3) + (-6x^2)$
$= (-x^3) + [-8x^2 + (-6x^2)] + (-10x)$
$= -x^3 - 14x^2 - 10x$

Exercises

Find each product.

1. $x(5x + x^2)$

2. $x(4x^2 + 3x + 2)$

3. $-2xy(2y + 4x^2)$

4. $-2g(g^2 - 2g + 2)$

5. $3x(x^4 + x^3 + x^2)$

6. $-4x(2x^3 - 2x + 3)$

7. $-4cx(10 + 3x)$

8. $3y(-4x - 6x^3 - 2y)$

9. $2x^2y^2(3xy + 2y + 5x)$

Simplify.

10. $x(3x - 4) - 5x$

11. $-x(2x^2 - 4x) - 6x^2$

12. $6a(2a - b) + 2a(-4a + 5b)$

13. $4r(2r^2 - 3r + 5) + 6r(4r^2 + 2r + 8)$

14. $4n(3n^2 + n - 4) - n(3 - n)$

15. $2b(b^2 + 4b + 8) - 3b(3b^2 + 9b - 18)$

16. $-2z(4z^2 - 3z + 1) - z(3z^2 + 2z - 1)$

17. $2(4x^2 - 2x) - 3(-6x^2 + 4) + 2x(x - 1)$

8-6 Study Guide and Intervention *(continued)*

Multiplying a Polynomial by a Monomial

Solve Equations with Polynomial Expressions Many equations contain polynomials that must be added, subtracted, or multiplied before the equation can be solved.

Example Solve $4(n - 2) + 5n = 6(3 - n) + 19$.

$4(n - 2) + 5n = 6(3 - n) + 19$	Original equation
$4n - 8 + 5n = 18 - 6n + 19$	Distributive Property
$9n - 8 = 37 - 6n$	Combine like terms.
$15n - 8 = 37$	Add 6n to both sides.
$15n = 45$	Add 8 to both sides.
$n = 3$	Divide each side by 15.

The solution is 3.

Exercises

Solve each equation.

1. $2(a - 3) = 3(-2a + 6)$

2. $3(x + 5) - 6 = 18$

3. $3x(x - 5) - 3x^2 = -30$

4. $6(x^2 + 2x) = 2(3x^2 + 12)$

5. $4(2p + 1) - 12p = 2(8p + 12)$

6. $2(6x + 4) + 2 = 4(x - 4)$

7. $-2(4y - 3) - 8y + 6 = 4(y - 2)$

8. $c(c + 2) - c(c - 6) = 10c - 12$

9. $3(x^2 - 2x) = 3x^2 + 5x - 11$

10. $2(4x + 3) + 2 = -4(x + 1)$

11. $3(2h - 6) - (2h + 1) = 9$

12. $3(y + 5) - (4y - 8) = -2y + 10$

13. $3(2a - 6) - (-3a - 1) = 4a - 2$

14. $5(2x^2 - 1) - (10x^2 - 6) = -(x + 2)$

15. $3(x + 2) + 2(x + 1) = -5(x - 3)$

16. $4(3p^2 + 2p) - 12p^2 = 2(8p + 6)$

8-7 Study Guide and Intervention

Multiplying Polynomials

Multiply Binomials To multiply two binomials, you can apply the Distributive Property twice. A useful way to keep track of terms in the product is to use the FOIL method as illustrated in Example 2.

Example 1 Find $(x + 3)(x - 4)$.

Horizontal Method

$(x + 3)(x - 4)$
$= x(x - 4) + 3(x - 4)$
$= (x)(x) + x(-4) + 3(x) + 3(-4)$
$= x^2 - 4x + 3x - 12$
$= x^2 - x - 12$

Vertical Method

$$
\begin{array}{r}
x + 3 \\
(\times) \quad x - 4 \\
\hline
-4x - 12 \\
x^2 + 3x \quad\quad \\
\hline
x^2 - x - 12
\end{array}
$$

The product is $x^2 - x - 12$.

Example 2 Find $(x - 2)(x + 5)$ using the FOIL method.

$(x - 2)(x + 5)$

       First   Outer   Inner   Last
$= (x)(x) + (x)(5) + (-2)(x) + (-2)(5)$
$= x^2 + 5x + (-2x) - 10$
$= x^2 + 3x - 10$

The product is $x^2 + 3x - 10$.

Exercises

Find each product.

1. $(x + 2)(x + 3)$

2. $(x - 4)(x + 1)$

3. $(x - 6)(x - 2)$

4. $(p - 4)(p + 2)$

5. $(y + 5)(y + 2)$

6. $(2x - 1)(x + 5)$

7. $(3n - 4)(3n - 4)$

8. $(8m - 2)(8m + 2)$

9. $(k + 4)(5k - 1)$

10. $(3x + 1)(4x + 3)$

11. $(x - 8)(-3x + 1)$

12. $(5t + 4)(2t - 6)$

13. $(5m - 3n)(4m - 2n)$

14. $(a - 3b)(2a - 5b)$

15. $(8x - 5)(8x + 5)$

16. $(2n - 4)(2n + 5)$

17. $(4m - 3)(5m - 5)$

18. $(7g - 4)(7g + 4)$

8-7 Study Guide and Intervention (continued)

Multiplying Polynomials

Multiply Polynomials The Distributive Property can be used to multiply any two polynomials.

Example Find $(3x + 2)(2x^2 - 4x + 5)$.

$(3x + 2)(2x^2 - 4x + 5)$

$\quad = 3x(2x^2 - 4x + 5) + 2(2x^2 - 4x + 5)$ Distributive Property

$\quad = 6x^3 - 12x^2 + 15x + 4x^2 - 8x + 10$ Distributive Property

$\quad = 6x^3 - 8x^2 + 7x + 10$ Combine like terms.

The product is $6x^3 - 8x^2 + 7x + 10$.

Exercises

Find each product.

1. $(x + 2)(x^2 - 2x + 1)$

2. $(x + 3)(2x^2 + x - 3)$

3. $(2x - 1)(x^2 - x + 2)$

4. $(p - 3)(p^2 - 4p + 2)$

5. $(3k + 2)(k^2 + k - 4)$

6. $(2t + 1)(10t^2 - 2t - 4)$

7. $(3n - 4)(n^2 + 5n - 4)$

8. $(8x - 2)(3x^2 + 2x - 1)$

9. $(2a + 4)(2a^2 - 8a + 3)$

10. $(3x - 4)(2x^2 + 3x + 3)$

11. $(n^2 + 2n - 1)(n^2 + n + 2)$

12. $(t^2 + 4t - 1)(2t^2 - t - 3)$

13. $(y^2 - 5y + 3)(2y^2 + 7y - 4)$

14. $(3b^2 - 2b + 1)(2b^2 - 3b - 4)$

8-8 Study Guide and Intervention

Special Products

Squares of Sums and Differences Some pairs of binomials have products that follow specific patterns. One such pattern is called the *square of a sum*. Another is called the *square of a difference*.

Square of a sum	$(a + b)^2 = (a + b)(a + b) = a^2 + 2ab + b^2$
Square of a difference	$(a - b)^2 = (a - b)(a - b) = a^2 - 2ab + b^2$

Example 1 Find $(3a + 4)(3a + 4)$.

Use the square of a sum pattern, with $a = 3a$ and $b = 4$.

$(3a + 4)(3a + 4) = (3a)^2 + 2(3a)(4) + (4)^2$
$= 9a^2 + 24a + 16$

The product is $9a^2 + 24a + 16$.

Example 2 Find $(2z - 9)(2z - 9)$.

Use the square of a difference pattern with $a = 2z$ and $b = 9$.

$(2z - 9)(2z - 9) = (2z)^2 - 2(2z)(9) + (9)(9)$
$= 4z^2 - 36z + 81$

The product is $4z^2 - 36z + 81$.

Exercises

Find each product.

1. $(x - 6)^2$

2. $(3p + 4)^2$

3. $(4x - 5)^2$

4. $(2x - 1)^2$

5. $(2h + 3)^2$

6. $(m + 5)^2$

7. $(c + 3)^2$

8. $(3 - p)^2$

9. $(x - 5y)^2$

10. $(8y + 4)^2$

11. $(8 + x)^2$

12. $(3a - 2b)^2$

13. $(2x - 8)^2$

14. $(x^2 + 1)^2$

15. $(m^2 - 2)^2$

16. $(x^3 - 1)^2$

17. $(2h^2 - k^2)^2$

18. $\left(\frac{1}{4}x + 3\right)^2$

19. $(x - 4y^2)^2$

20. $(2p + 4q)^2$

21. $\left(\frac{2}{3}x - 2\right)^2$

Lesson 8-8

8-8 Study Guide and Intervention *(continued)*

Special Products

Product of a Sum and a Difference There is also a pattern for the product of a sum and a difference of the same two terms, $(a + b)(a - b)$. The product is called the **difference of squares**.

Product of a Sum and a Difference	$(a + b)(a - b) = a^2 - b^2$

Example Find $(5x + 3y)(5x - 3y)$.

$(a + b)(a - b) = a^2 - b^2$ Product of a Sum and a Difference

$(5x + 3y)(5x - 3y) = (5x)^2 - (3y)^2$ $a = 5x$ and $b = 3y$

$\qquad\qquad\qquad = 25x^2 - 9y^2$ Simplify.

The product is $25x^2 - 9y^2$.

Exercises

Find each product.

1. $(x - 4)(x + 4)$ **2.** $(p + 2)(p - 2)$ **3.** $(4x - 5)(4x + 5)$

4. $(2x - 1)(2x + 1)$ **5.** $(h + 7)(h - 7)$ **6.** $(m - 5)(m + 5)$

7. $(2c - 3)(2c + 3)$ **8.** $(3 - 5q)(3 + 5q)$ **9.** $(x - y)(x + y)$

10. $(y - 4x)(y + 4x)$ **11.** $(8 + 4x)(8 - 4x)$ **12.** $(3a - 2b)(3a + 2b)$

13. $(3y - 8)(3y + 8)$ **14.** $(x^2 - 1)(x^2 + 1)$ **15.** $(m^2 - 5)(m^2 + 5)$

16. $(x^3 - 2)(x^3 + 2)$ **17.** $(h^2 - k^2)(h^2 + k^2)$ **18.** $\left(\frac{1}{4}x + 2\right)\left(\frac{1}{4}x - 2\right)$

19. $(3x - 2y^2)(3x + 2y^2)$ **20.** $(2p - 5s)(2p + 5s)$ **21.** $\left(\frac{4}{3}x - 2y\right)\left(\frac{4}{3}x + 2y\right)$

9-1 Study Guide and Intervention

Factors and Greatest Common Factors

Prime Factorization When two or more numbers are multiplied, each number is called a **factor** of the product.

	Definition	Example
Prime Number	A prime number is a whole number, greater than 1, whose only factors are 1 and itself.	5
Composite Number	A composite number is a whole number, greater than 1, that has more than two factors.	10
Prime Factorization	Prime factorization occurs when a whole number is expressed as a product of factors that are all prime numbers.	$45 = 3^2 \cdot 5$

Example 1 Factor each number. Then classify each number as *prime* or *composite*.

a. 28

To find the factors of 28, list all pairs of whole numbers whose product is 28.

$1 \times 28 \quad 2 \times 14 \quad 4 \times 7$

Therefore, the factors of 28 are 1, 2, 4, 7, 14, and 28. Since 28 has more than 2 factors, it is a composite number.

b. 31

To find the factors of 31, list all pairs of whole numbers whose product is 31.

1×31

Therefore, the factors of 31 are 1 and 31. Since the only factors of 31 are itself and 1, it is a prime number.

Example 2 Find the prime factorization of 200.

Method 1

$$200 = 2 \cdot 100$$
$$= 2 \cdot 2 \cdot 50$$
$$= 2 \cdot 2 \cdot 2 \cdot 25$$
$$= 2 \cdot 2 \cdot 2 \cdot 5 \cdot 5$$

All the factors in the last row are prime, so the prime factorization of 200 is $2^3 \cdot 5^2$.

Method 2

Use a factor tree.

All of the factors in each last branch of the factor tree are prime, so the prime factorization of 200 is $2^3 \cdot 5^2$.

Exercises

Find the factors of each number. Then classify the number as *prime* or *composite*.

1. 41

2. 121

3. 90

4. 2865

Find the prime factorization of each integer.

5. 600

6. 175

7. -150

Factor each monomial completely.

8. $32x^2$

9. $18m^2n$

10. $49a^3b^2$

9-1 Study Guide and Intervention (continued)

Factors and Greatest Common Factors

Greatest Common Factor

Greatest Common Factor (GCF)	
Integers	the greatest number that is a factor of all the integers
Monomials	the product of their common factors when each monomial is expressed in factored form

If two or more integers or monomials have no common prime factors, their GCF is 1 and the integers or monomials are said to be **relatively prime**.

Example Find the GCF of each set of monomials.

a. 12 and 18

$12 = ②· 2 ·③$ Factor each number.
$18 = ②·③· 3$ Circle the common prime factors, if any.
The GCF of 12 and 18 is $2 · 3$ or 6.

b. $16xy^2z^2$ and $72xyz^3$

$16xy^2z^2 = ②·②·②· 2 ·ⓧ·ⓨ· y ·ⓩ·ⓩ$
$72xyz^3 = ②·②·②· 3 · 3 ·ⓧ·ⓨ·ⓩ·ⓩ· z$
The GCF of $16xy^2z^2$ and $72xyz^3$ is $2 · 2 · 2 · x · y · z · z$ or $8xyz^2$.

Exercises

Find the GCF of each set of monomials.

1. 12, 48

2. 18, 42

3. 64, 80

4. 32, 54

5. 27, 32

6. 44, 100

7. 45, 15

8. 169, 13

9. 20, 440

10. $49x, 343x^2$

11. $4a^7b, 28ab$

12. $96y, 12x, 8y$

13. $12a, 18abc$

14. $28y^2, 35xy, 49x^2yz$

15. $2m^2n, 12mn^2, 18mn$

16. $12x^2, 32x^2yz, 60xy^2$

17. $18a^3b^2, 36a^3b^2$

18. $15mn^2, 30m^3n^2, 90m^3$

19. $2x^2y, 9x^2y^3, 18xy^2$

20. $a^4b, 8a^3b^2$

21. $ab^2, 5a^4b^2, 10b^3$

9-2 Study Guide and Intervention

Factoring Using the Distributive Property

Factor by Using the Distributive Property The Distributive Property has been used to multiply a polynomial by a monomial. It can also be used to express a polynomial in factored form. Compare the two columns in the table below.

Multiplying	Factoring
$3(a + b) = 3a + 3b$	$3a + 3b = 3(a + b)$
$x(y - z) = xy - xz$	$xy - xz = x(y - z)$
$6y(2x + 1) = 6y(2x) + 6y(1)$ $= 12xy + 6y$	$12xy + 6y = 6y(2x) + 6y(1)$ $= 6y(2x + 1)$

Example 1 Use the Distributive Property to factor $12mn + 80m^2$.

Find the GCF of $12mn$ and $80m^2$.

$12mn = 2 \cdot 2 \cdot 3 \cdot m \cdot n$
$80m^2 = 2 \cdot 2 \cdot 2 \cdot 2 \cdot 5 \cdot m \cdot m$
GCF $= 2 \cdot 2 \cdot m$ or $4m$

Write each term as the product of the GCF and its remaining factors.

$12mn + 80m^2 = 4m(3 \cdot n) + 4m(2 \cdot 2 \cdot 5 \cdot m)$
$= 4m(3n) + 4m(20m)$
$= 4m(3n + 20m)$

Thus $12mn + 80m^2 = 4m(3n + 20m)$.

Example 2 Factor $6ax + 3ay + 2bx + by$ by grouping.

$6ax + 3ay + 2bx + by$
$= (6ax + 3ay) + (2bx + by)$
$= 3a(2x + y) + b(2x + y)$
$= (3a + b)(2x + y)$

Check using the FOIL method.

$(3a + b)(2x + y)$
$= 3a(2x) + (3a)(y) + (b)(2x) + (b)(y)$
$= 6ax + 3ay + 2bx + by$ ✓

Exercises

Factor each polynomial.

1. $24x + 48y$

2. $30mn^2 + m^2n - 6n$

3. $q^4 - 18q^3 + 22q$

4. $9x^2 - 3x$

5. $4m + 6n - 8mn$

6. $45s^3 - 15s^2$

7. $14c^3 - 42c^5 - 49c^4$

8. $55p^2 - 11p^4 + 44p^5$

9. $14y^3 - 28y^2 + y$

10. $4x + 12x^2 + 16x^3$

11. $4a^2b + 28ab^2 + 7ab$

12. $6y + 12x - 8z$

13. $x^2 + 2x + x + 2$

14. $6y^2 - 4y + 3y - 2$

15. $4m^2 + 4mn + 3mn + 3n^2$

16. $12ax + 3xz + 4ay + yz$

17. $12a^2 + 3a - 8a - 2$

18. $xa + ya + x + y$

Lesson 9-2

9-2 Study Guide and Intervention (continued)

Factoring Using the Distributive Property

Solve Equations by Factoring The following property, along with factoring, can be used to solve certain equations.

Zero Product Property	For any real numbers a and b, if $ab = 0$, then either $a = 0$, $b = 0$, or both a and b equal 0.

Example **Solve $9x^2 + x = 0$. Then check the solutions.**

Write the equation so that it is of the form $ab = 0$.

$9x^2 + x = 0$	Original equation
$x(9x + 1) = 0$	Factor the GCF of $9x^2 + x$, which is x.
$x = 0$ or $9x + 1 = 0$	Zero Product Property
$x = 0 \qquad x = -\dfrac{1}{9}$	Solve each equation.

The solution set is $\left\{0, -\dfrac{1}{9}\right\}$.

CHECK Substitute 0 and $-\dfrac{1}{9}$ for x in the original equation.

$$9x^2 + x = 0 \qquad\qquad 9x^2 + x = 0$$
$$9(0)^2 + 0 = 0 \qquad 9\left(-\dfrac{1}{9}\right)^2 + \left(-\dfrac{1}{9}\right) = 0$$
$$0 = 0 \checkmark \qquad\qquad \dfrac{1}{9} + \left(-\dfrac{1}{9}\right) = 0$$
$$0 = 0 \checkmark$$

Exercises

Solve each equation. Check your solutions.

1. $x(x + 3) = 0$

2. $3m(m - 4) = 0$

3. $(r - 3)(r + 2) = 0$

4. $3x(2x - 1) = 0$

5. $(4m + 8)(m - 3) = 0$

6. $5s^2 = 25s$

7. $(4c + 2)(2c - 7) = 0$

8. $5p - 15p^2 = 0$

9. $4y^2 = 28y$

10. $12x^2 = -6x$

11. $(4a + 3)(8a + 7) = 0$

12. $8y = 12y^2$

13. $x^2 = -2x$

14. $(6y - 4)(y + 3) = 0$

15. $4m^2 = 4m$

16. $12x = 3x^2$

17. $12a^2 = -3a$

18. $(12a + 4)(3a - 1) = 0$

9-3 Study Guide and Intervention

Factoring Trinomials: $x^2 + bx + c$

Factor $x^2 + bx + c$ To factor a trinomial of the form $x^2 + bx + c$, find two integers, m and n, whose sum is equal to b and whose product is equal to c.

Factoring $x^2 + bx + c$	$x^2 + bx + c = (x + m)(x + n)$, where $m + n = b$ and $mn = c$.

Example 1 Factor each trinomial.

a. $x^2 + 7x + 10$

In this trinomial, $b = 7$ and $c = 10$.

Factors of 10	Sum of Factors
1, 10	11
2, 5	7

Since $2 + 5 = 7$ and $2 \cdot 5 = 10$, let $m = 2$ and $n = 5$.

$x^2 + 7x + 10 = (x + 5)(x + 2)$

b. $x^2 - 8x + 7$

In this trinomial, $b = -8$ and $c = 7$. Notice that $m + n$ is negative and mn is positive, so m and n are both negative. Since $-7 + (-1) = -8$ and $(-7)(-1) = 7$, $m = -7$ and $n = -1$.

$x^2 - 8x + 7 = (x - 7)(x - 1)$

Example 2 Factor $x^2 + 6x - 16$.

In this trinomial, $b = 6$ and $c = -16$. This means $m + n$ is positive and mn is negative. Make a list of the factors of -16, where one factor of each pair is positive.

Factors of -16	Sum of Factors
1, -16	-15
-1, 16	15
2, -8	-6
-2, 8	6

Therefore, $m = -2$ and $n = 8$.
$x^2 + 6x - 16 = (x - 2)(x + 8)$

Exercises

Factor each trinomial.

1. $x^2 + 4x + 3$

2. $m^2 + 12m + 32$

3. $r^2 - 3r + 2$

4. $x^2 - x - 6$

5. $x^2 - 4x - 21$

6. $x^2 - 22x + 121$

7. $c^2 - 4c - 12$

8. $p^2 - 16p + 64$

9. $9 - 10x + x^2$

10. $x^2 + 6x + 5$

11. $a^2 + 8a - 9$

12. $y^2 - 7y - 8$

13. $x^2 - 2x - 3$

14. $y^2 + 14y + 13$

15. $m^2 + 9m + 20$

16. $x^2 + 12x + 20$

17. $a^2 - 14a + 24$

18. $18 + 11y + y^2$

19. $x^2 + 2xy + y^2$

20. $a^2 - 4ab + 4b^2$

21. $x^2 + 6xy - 7y^2$

Lesson 9-3

9-3 Study Guide and Intervention (continued)

Factoring Trinomials: $x^2 + bx + c$

Solve Equations by Factoring Factoring and the Zero Product Property from Lesson 9-2 can be used to solve many equations of the form $x^2 + bx + c = 0$.

Example 1 Solve $x^2 + 6x = 7$. Check your solutions.

$x^2 + 6x = 7$	Original equation
$x^2 + 6x - 7 = 0$	Rewrite equation so that one side equals 0.
$(x - 1)(x + 7) = 0$	Factor.
$x - 1 = 0$ or $x + 7 = 0$	Zero Product Property
$x = 1$ $x = -7$	Solve each equation.

The solution set is $\{1, -7\}$. Since $1^2 + 6 = 7$ and $(-7)^2 + 6(-7) = 7$, the solutions check.

Example 2 **ROCKET LAUNCH** A rocket is fired with an initial velocity of 2288 feet per second. How many seconds will it take for the rocket to hit the ground?

The formula $h = vt - 16t^2$ gives the height h of the rocket after t seconds when the initial velocity v is given in feet per second.

$h = vt - 16t^2$	Formula
$0 = 2288t - 16t^2$	Substitute.
$0 = 16t(143 - t)$	Factor.
$16t = 0$ or $143 - t = 0$	Zero Product Property
$t = 0$ $t = 143$	Solve each equation.

The value $t = 0$ represents the time at launch. The rocket returns to the ground in 143 seconds, or a little less than 2.5 minutes after launch.

Exercises

Solve each equation. Check your solutions.

1. $x^2 - 4x + 3 = 0$ 2. $y^2 - 5y + 4 = 0$ 3. $m^2 + 10m + 9 = 0$

4. $x^2 = x + 2$ 5. $x^2 - 4x = 5$ 6. $x^2 - 12x + 36 = 0$

7. $c^2 - 8 = -7c$ 8. $p^2 = 9p - 14$ 9. $-9 - 8x + x^2 = 0$

10. $x^2 + 6 = 5x$ 11. $a^2 = 11a - 18$ 12. $y^2 - 8y + 15 = 0$

13. $x^2 = 24 - 10x$ 14. $a^2 - 18a = -72$ 15. $b^2 = 10b - 16$

Use the formula $h = vt - 16t^2$ to solve each problem.

16. **FOOTBALL** A punter can kick a football with an initial velocity of 48 feet per second. How many seconds will it take for the ball to return to the ground?

17. **BASEBALL** A ball is thrown up with an initial velocity of 32 feet per second. How many seconds will it take for the ball to return to the ground?

18. **ROCKET LAUNCH** If a rocket is launched with an initial velocity of 1600 feet per second, when will the rocket be 14,400 feet high?

9-4 Study Guide and Intervention

Factoring Trinomials: $ax^2 + bx + c$

Factor $ax^2 + bx + c$ To factor a trinomial of the form $ax^2 + bx + c$, find two integers, m and n whose product is equal to ac and whose sum is equal to b. If there are no integers that satisfy these requirements, the polynomial is called a **prime polynomial**.

Example 1 Factor $2x^2 + 15x + 18$.

In this example, $a = 2$, $b = 15$, and $c = 18$. You need to find two numbers whose sum is 15 and whose product is $2 \cdot 18$ or 36. Make a list of the factors of 36 and look for the pair of factors whose sum is 15.

Factors of 36	Sum of Factors
1, 36	37
2, 18	20
3, 12	15

Use the pattern $ax^2 + mx + nx + c$, with $a = 2$, $m = 3$, $n = 12$, and $c = 18$.

$2x^2 + 15x + 18 = 2x^2 + 3x + 12x + 18$
$= (2x^2 + 3x) + (12x + 18)$
$= x(2x + 3) + 6(2x + 3)$
$= (x + 6)(2x + 3)$

Therefore, $2x^2 + 15x + 18 = (x + 6)(2x + 3)$.

Example 2 Factor $3x^2 - 3x - 18$.

Note that the GCF of the terms $3x^2$, $3x$, and 18 is 3. First factor out this GCF.

$3x^2 - 3x - 18 = 3(x^2 - x - 6)$.

Now factor $x^2 - x - 6$. Since $a = 1$, find the two factors of -6 whose sum is -1.

Factors of -6	Sum of Factors
1, -6	-5
-1, 6	5
-2, 3	1
2, -3	-1

Now use the pattern $(x + m)(x + n)$ with $m = 2$ and $n = -3$.
$x^2 - x - 6 = (x + 2)(x - 3)$

The complete factorization is
$3x^2 - 3x - 18 = 3(x + 2)(x - 3)$.

Exercises

Factor each trinomial, if possible. If the trinomial cannot be factored using integers, write *prime*.

1. $2x^2 - 3x - 2$

2. $3m^2 - 8m - 3$

3. $16r^2 - 8r + 1$

4. $6x^2 + 5x - 6$

5. $3x^2 + 2x - 8$

6. $18x^2 - 27x - 5$

7. $2a^2 + 5a + 3$

8. $18y^2 + 9y - 5$

9. $-4c^2 + 19c - 21$

10. $8x^2 - 4x - 24$

11. $28p^2 + 60p - 25$

12. $48x^2 + 22x - 15$

13. $3y^2 - 6y - 24$

14. $4x^2 + 26x - 48$

15. $8m^2 - 44m + 48$

16. $6x^2 - 7x + 18$

17. $2a^2 - 14a + 18$

18. $18 + 11y + 2y^2$

9-4 Study Guide and Intervention (continued)

Factoring Trinomials: $ax^2 + bx + c$

Solve Equations by Factoring Factoring and the Zero Product Property can be used to solve some equations of the form $ax^2 + bx + c = 0$.

Example Solve $12x^2 + 3x = 2 - 2x$. Check your solutions.

$12x^2 + 3x = 2 - 2x$	Original equation
$12x^2 + 5x - 2 = 0$	Rewrite equation so that one side equals 0.
$(3x + 2)(4x - 1) = 0$	Factor the left side.
$3x + 2 = 0$ or $4x - 1 = 0$	Zero Product Property
$x = -\dfrac{2}{3}$ $x = \dfrac{1}{4}$	Solve each equation.

The solution set is $\left\{-\dfrac{2}{3}, \dfrac{1}{4}\right\}$.

Since $12\left(-\dfrac{2}{3}\right)^2 + 3\left(-\dfrac{2}{3}\right) = 2 - 2\left(-\dfrac{2}{3}\right)$ and $12\left(\dfrac{1}{4}\right)^2 + 3\left(\dfrac{1}{4}\right) = 2 - 2\left(\dfrac{1}{4}\right)$, the solutions check.

Exercises

Solve each equation. Check your solutions.

1. $8x^2 + 2x - 3 = 0$

2. $3n^2 - 2n - 5 = 0$

3. $2d^2 - 13d - 7 = 0$

4. $4x^2 = x + 3$

5. $3x^2 - 13x = 10$

6. $6x^2 - 11x - 10 = 0$

7. $2k^2 - 40 = -11k$

8. $2p^2 = -21p - 40$

9. $-7 - 18x + 9x^2 = 0$

10. $12x^2 - 15 = -8x$

11. $7a^2 = -65a - 18$

12. $16y^2 - 2y - 3 = 0$

13. $8x^2 + 5x = 3 + 7x$

14. $4a^2 - 18a + 5 = 15$

15. $3b^2 - 18b = 10b - 49$

16. The difference of the squares of two consecutive odd integers is 24. Find the integers.

17. GEOMETRY The length of a Charlotte, North Carolina, conservatory garden is 20 yards greater than its width. The area is 300 square yards. What are the dimensions?

18. GEOMETRY A rectangle with an area of 24 square inches is formed by cutting strips of equal width from a rectangular piece of paper. Find the dimensions of the new rectangle if the original rectangle measures 8 inches by 6 inches.

9-5 Study Guide and Intervention

Factoring Differences of Squares

Factor $a^2 - b^2$ The binomial expression $a^2 - b^2$ is called the **difference of two squares**. The following pattern shows how to factor the difference of squares.

Difference of Squares	$a^2 - b^2 = (a - b)(a + b) = (a + b)(a - b)$.

Example 1 Factor each binomial.

a. $n^2 - 64$

$n^2 - 64$

$= n^2 - 8^2$ Write in the form $a^2 - b^2$.

$= (n + 8)(n - 8)$ Factor.

b. $4m^2 - 81n^2$

$4m^2 - 81n^2$

$= (2m)^2 - (9n)^2$ Write in the form $a^2 - b^2$.

$= (2m - 9n)(2m + 9n)$ Factor.

Example 2 Factor each polynomial.

a. $50a^2 - 72$

$50a^2 - 72$

$= 2(25a^2 - 36)$ Find the GCF.

$= 2[(5a)^2 - 6^2)]$ $25a^2 = 5a \cdot 5a$ and $36 = 6 \cdot 6$

$= 2(5a + 6)(5a - 6)$ Factor the difference of squares.

b. $4x^4 + 8x^3 - 4x^2 - 8x$

$4x^4 + 8x^3 - 4x^2 - 8x$ Original polynomial

$= 4x(x^3 + 2x^2 - x - 2)$ Find the GCF.

$= 4x[(x^3 + 2x^2) - (x + 2)]$ Group terms.

$= 4x[x^2(x + 2) - 1(x + 2)]$ Find the GCF.

$= 4x[(x^2 - 1)(x + 2)]$ Factor by grouping.

$= 4x[(x - 1)(x + 1)(x + 2)]$ Factor the difference of squares.

Exercises

Factor each polynomial if possible. If the polynomial cannot be factored, write *prime*.

1. $x^2 - 81$

2. $m^2 - 100$

3. $16n^2 - 25$

4. $36x^2 - 100y^2$

5. $49x^2 - 32$

6. $16a^2 - 9b^2$

7. $225c^2 - a^2$

8. $72p^2 - 50$

9. $-2 + 2x^2$

10. $-81 + a^4$

11. $6 - 54a^2$

12. $8y^2 - 200$

13. $4x^3 - 100x$

14. $2y^4 - 32y^2$

15. $8m^3 - 128m$

16. $6x^2 - 25$

17. $2a^3 - 98ab^2$

18. $18y^2 - 72y^4$

19. $169x^3 - x$

20. $3a^4 - 3a^2$

21. $3x^4 + 6x^3 - 3x^2 - 6x$

Lesson 9-5

9-5 Study Guide and Intervention (continued)

Factoring Differences of Squares

Solve Equations by Factoring Factoring and the Zero Product Property can be used to solve equations that can be written as the product of any number of factors set equal to 0.

Example **Solve each equation. Check your solutions.**

a. $x^2 - \dfrac{1}{25} = 0$

$x^2 - \dfrac{1}{25} = 0$ Original equation

$x^2 - \left(\dfrac{1}{5}\right)^2 = 0$ $x^2 = x \cdot x$ and $\dfrac{1}{25} = \left(\dfrac{1}{5}\right)\left(\dfrac{1}{5}\right)$

$\left(x + \dfrac{1}{5}\right)\left(x - \dfrac{1}{5}\right) = 0$ Factor the difference of squares.

$x + \dfrac{1}{5} = 0$ or $x - \dfrac{1}{5} = 0$ Zero Product Property

$x = -\dfrac{1}{5}$ $x = \dfrac{1}{5}$ Solve each equation.

The solution set is $\left\{-\dfrac{1}{5}, \dfrac{1}{5}\right\}$. Since $\left(-\dfrac{1}{5}\right)^2 - \dfrac{1}{25} = 0$ and $\left(\dfrac{1}{5}\right)^2 - \dfrac{1}{25} = 0$, the solutions check.

b. $4x^3 = 9x$

$4x^3 = 9x$ Original equation
$4x^3 - 9x = 0$ Subtract $9x$ from each side.
$x(4x^2 - 9) = 0$ Find the GCF.
$x[(2x)^2 - 3^2] = 0$ $4x^2 = 2x \cdot 2x$ and $9 = 3 \cdot 3$
$x[(2x)^2 - 3^2] = x[(2x - 3)(2x + 3)]$ Factor the difference of squares.
$x = 0$ or $(2x - 3) = 0$ or $(2x + 3) = 0$ Zero Product Property
$x = 0$ $x = \dfrac{3}{2}$ $x = -\dfrac{3}{2}$ Solve each equation.

The solution set is $\left\{0, \dfrac{3}{2}, -\dfrac{3}{2}\right\}$.

Since $4(0)^3 = 9(0)$, $4\left(\dfrac{3}{2}\right)^3 = 9\left(\dfrac{3}{2}\right)$, and $4\left(-\dfrac{3}{2}\right)^3 = 9\left(-\dfrac{3}{2}\right)$, the solutions check.

Exercises

Solve each equation. Check your solutions.

1. $81x^2 = 49$ **2.** $36n^2 = 1$ **3.** $25d^2 - 100 = 0$

4. $\dfrac{1}{4}x^2 = 25$ **5.** $36 = \dfrac{1}{25}x^2$ **6.** $\dfrac{49}{100} - x^2 = 0$

7. $9x^3 = 25x$ **8.** $7a^3 = 175a$ **9.** $2m^3 = 32m$

10. $16y^3 = 25y$ **11.** $\dfrac{1}{64}x^2 = 49$ **12.** $4a^3 - 64a = 0$

13. $3b^3 - 27b = 0$ **14.** $\dfrac{9}{25}m^2 = 121$ **15.** $48n^3 = 147n$

9-6 Study Guide and Intervention
Perfect Squares and Factoring

Factor Perfect Square Trinomials

Perfect Square Trinomial	a trinomial of the form $a^2 + 2ab + b^2$ or $a^2 - 2ab + b^2$

The patterns shown below can be used to factor perfect square trinomials.

Squaring a Binomial	Factoring a Perfect Square Trinomial
$(a + 4)^2 = a^2 + 2(a)(4) + 4^2$ $= a^2 + 8a + 16$	$a^2 + 8a + 16 = a^2 + 2(a)(4) + 4^2$ $= (a + 4)^2$
$(2x - 3)^2 = (2x)^2 - 2(2x)(3) + 3^2$ $= 4x^2 - 12x + 9$	$4x^2 - 12x + 9 = (2x)^2 - 2(2x)(3) + 3^2$ $= (2x - 3)^2$

Example 1 Determine whether $16n^2 - 24n + 9$ is a perfect square trinomial. If so, factor it.

Since $16n^2 = (4n)(4n)$, the first term is a perfect square.
Since $9 = 3 \cdot 3$, the last term is a perfect square.
The middle term is equal to $2(4n)(3)$.
Therefore, $16n^2 - 24n + 9$ is a perfect square trinomial.

$16n^2 - 24n + 9 = (4n)^2 - 2(4n)(3) + 3^2$
$= (4n - 3)^2$

Example 2 Factor $16x^2 - 32x + 15$.

Since 15 is not a perfect square, use a different factoring pattern.

$16x^2 - 32x + 15$	Original trinomial
$= 16x^2 + mx + nx + 15$	Write the pattern.
$= 16x^2 - 12x - 20x + 15$	$m = -12$ and $n = -20$
$= (16x^2 - 12x) - (20x - 15)$	Group terms.
$= 4x(4x - 3) - 5(4x - 3)$	Find the GCF.
$= (4x - 5)(4x - 3)$	Factor by grouping.

Therefore $16x^2 - 32x + 15 = (4x - 5)(4x - 3)$.

Exercises

Determine whether each trinomial is a perfect square trinomial. If so, factor it.

1. $x^2 - 16x + 64$

2. $m^2 + 10m + 25$

3. $p^2 + 8p + 64$

Factor each polynomial if possible. If the polynomial cannot be factored, write **prime**.

4. $98x^2 - 200y^2$

5. $x^2 + 22x + 121$

6. $81 + 18s + s^2$

7. $25c^2 - 10c - 1$

8. $169 - 26r + r^2$

9. $7x^2 - 9x + 2$

10. $16m^2 + 48m + 36$

11. $16 - 25a^2$

12. $b^2 - 16b + 256$

13. $36x^2 - 12x + 1$

14. $16a^2 - 40ab + 25b^2$

15. $8m^3 - 64m$

9-6 Study Guide and Intervention *(continued)*

Perfect Squares and Factoring

Solve Equations with Perfect Squares Factoring and the Zero Product Property can be used to solve equations that involve repeated factors. The repeated factor gives just one solution to the equation. You may also be able to use the **square root property** below to solve certain equations.

Square Root Property	For any number $n > 0$, if $x^2 = n$, then $x = \pm\sqrt{n}$.

Example **Solve each equation. Check your solutions.**

a. $x^2 - 6x + 9 = 0$

$$x^2 - 6x + 9 = 0 \qquad \text{Original equation}$$
$$x^2 - 2(3x) + 3^2 = 0 \qquad \text{Recognize a perfect square trinomial.}$$
$$(x - 3)(x - 3) = 0 \qquad \text{Factor the perfect square trinomial.}$$
$$x - 3 = 0 \qquad \text{Set repeated factor equal to 0.}$$
$$x = 3 \qquad \text{Solve.}$$

The solution set is {3}. Since $3^2 - 6(3) + 9 = 0$, the solution checks.

b. $(a - 5)^2 = 64$

$$(a - 5)^2 = 64 \qquad \text{Original equation}$$
$$a - 5 = \pm\sqrt{64} \qquad \text{Square Root Property}$$
$$a - 5 = \pm 8 \qquad 64 = 8 \cdot 8$$
$$a = 5 \pm 8 \qquad \text{Add 5 to each side.}$$
$$a = 5 + 8 \quad \text{or} \quad a = 5 - 8 \qquad \text{Separate into 2 equations.}$$
$$a = 13 \qquad\qquad a = -3 \qquad \text{Solve each equation.}$$

The solution set is {−3, 13}. Since $(-3 - 5)^2 = 64$ and $(13 - 5)^2 = 64$, the solutions check.

Exercises

Solve each equation. Check your solutions.

1. $x^2 + 4x + 4 = 0$

2. $16n^2 + 16n + 4 = 0$

3. $25d^2 - 10d + 1 = 0$

4. $x^2 + 10x + 25 = 0$

5. $9x^2 - 6x + 1 = 0$

6. $x^2 + x + \dfrac{1}{4} = 0$

7. $25k^2 + 20k + 4 = 0$

8. $p^2 + 2p + 1 = 49$

9. $x^2 + 4x + 4 = 64$

10. $x^2 - 6x + 9 = 25$

11. $a^2 + 8a + 16 = 1$

12. $16y^2 + 8y + 1 = 0$

13. $(x + 3)^2 = 49$

14. $(y + 6)^2 = 1$

15. $(m - 7)^2 = 49$

16. $(2x + 1)^2 = 1$

17. $(4x + 3)^2 = 25$

18. $(3h - 2)^2 = 4$

19. $(x + 1)^2 = 7$

20. $(y - 3)^2 = 6$

21. $(m - 2)^2 = 5$

10-1 Study Guide and Intervention

Graphing Quadratic Functions

Graph Quadratic Functions

Quadratic Function	a function described by an equation of the form $f(x) = ax^2 + bx + c$, where $a \neq 0$	Example: $y = 2x^2 + 3x + 8$

The degree of a quadratic function is 2, and the exponents are positive. Graphs of quadratic functions have a general shape called a **parabola**. A parabola opens upward and has a **minimum point** when the value of a is positive, and a parabola opens downward and has a **maximum point** when the value of a is negative.

Example 1 Use a table of values to graph $y = x^2 - 4x + 1$.

x	y
−1	6
0	1
1	−2
2	−3
3	−2
4	1

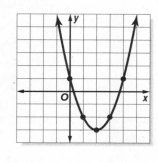

Graph the ordered pairs in the table and connect them with a smooth curve.

Example 2 Use a table of values to graph $y = -x^2 - 6x - 7$.

x	y
−6	−7
−5	−2
−4	1
−3	2
−2	1
−1	−2
0	−7

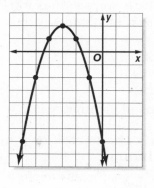

Graph the ordered pairs in the table and connect them with a smooth curve.

Exercises

Use a table of values to graph each function.

1. $y = x^2 + 2$

2. $y = -x^2 - 4$

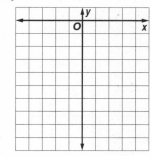

3. $y = x^2 - 3x + 2$

10-1 Study Guide and Intervention (continued)

Graphing Quadratic Functions

Symmetry and Vertices Parabolas have a geometric property called **symmetry**. That is, if the figure is folded in half, each half will match the other half exactly. The vertical line containing the fold line is called the **axis of symmetry**.

Axis of Symmetry	For the parabola $y = ax^2 + bx + c$, where $a \neq 0$, the line $x = -\dfrac{b}{2a}$ is the axis of symmetry.	**Example:** The axis of symmetry of $y = x^2 + 2x + 5$ is the line $x = -1$.

The axis of symmetry contains the minimum or maximum point of the parabola, the **vertex**.

Example Consider the graph of $y = 2x^2 + 4x + 1$.

a. Write the equation of the axis of symmetry.

In $y = 2x^2 + 4x + 1$, $a = 2$ and $b = 4$. Substitute these values into the equation of the axis of symmetry.

$$x = -\frac{b}{2a}$$

$$x = -\frac{4}{2(2)} = -1$$

The axis of symmetry is $x = -1$.

b. Find the coordinates of the vertex.

Since the equation of the axis of symmetry is $x = -1$ and the vertex lies on the axis, the x-coordinate of the vertex is -1.

$y = 2x^2 + 4x + 1$	Original equation
$y = 2(-1)^2 + 4(-1) + 1$	Substitute.
$y = 2(1) - 4 + 1$	Simplify.
$y = -1$	

The vertex is at $(-1, -1)$.

c. Identify the vertex as a maximum or a minimum.

Since the coefficient of the x^2-term is positive, the parabola opens upward, and the vertex is a minimum point.

d. Graph the function.

Exercises

Write the equation of the axis of symmetry, and find the coordinates of the vertex of the graph of each function. Identify the vertex as a maximum or a minimum. Then graph the function.

1. $y = x^2 + 3$

2. $y = -x^2 - 4x - 4$

3. $y = x^2 + 2x + 3$

10-2 Study Guide and Intervention

Solving Quadratic Equations by Graphing

Solve by Graphing

Quadratic Equation	an equation of the form $ax^2 + bx + c = 0$, where $a \neq 0$

The solutions of a quadratic equation are called the **roots** of the equation. The roots of a quadratic equation can be found by graphing the related quadratic function $f(x) = ax^2 + bx + c$ and finding the x-intercepts or **zeros** of the function.

Example 1 Solve $x^2 + 4x + 3 = 0$ by graphing.

Graph the related function $f(x) = x^2 + 4x + 3$. The equation of the axis of symmetry is $x = -\frac{4}{2(1)}$ or -2. The vertex is at $(-2, -1)$. Graph the vertex and several other points on either side of the axis of symmetry.

To solve $x^2 + 4x + 3 = 0$, you need to know where the value of $f(x) = 0$. This occurs at the x-intercepts, -3 and -1.
The solutions are -3 and -1.

Example 2 Solve $x^2 - 6x + 9 = 0$ by graphing.

Graph the related function $f(x) = x^2 - 6x + 9$. The equation of the axis of symmetry is $x = \frac{6}{2(1)}$ or 3. The vertex is at $(3, 0)$. Graph the vertex and several other points on either side of the axis of symmetry.

To solve $x^2 - 6x + 9 = 0$, you need to know where the value of $f(x) = 0$. The vertex of the parabola is the x-intercept. Thus, the only solution is 3.

Exercises

Solve each equation by graphing.

1. $x^2 + 7x + 12 = 0$

2. $x^2 - x - 12 = 0$

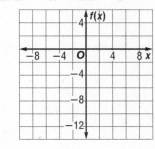

3. $x^2 - 4x + 5 = 0$

    133   *Glencoe Algebra 1*

Lesson 10-2

10-2 **Study Guide and Intervention** *(continued)*

Solving Quadratic Equations by Graphing

Estimate Solutions The roots of a quadratic equation may not be integers. If exact roots cannot be found, they can be estimated by finding the consecutive integers between which the roots lie.

Example Solve $x^2 + 6x + 6 = 0$ by graphing. If integral roots cannot be found, estimate the roots by stating the consecutive integers between which the roots lie.

Graph the related function $f(x) = x^2 + 6x + 6$.

x	f(x)
−5	1
−4	−2
−3	−3
−2	−2
−1	1

Notice that the value of the function changes from negative to positive between the x-values of −5 and −4 and between −2 and −1.

The x-intercepts of the graph are between −5 and −4 and between −2 and −1.
So one root is between −5 and −4, and the other root is between −2 and −1.

Exercises

Solve each equation by graphing. If integral roots cannot be found, estimate the roots by stating the consecutive integers between which the roots lie.

1. $x^2 + 7x + 9 = 0$

2. $x^2 - x - 4 = 0$

3. $x^2 - 4x + 6 = 0$

4. $x^2 - 4x - 1 = 0$

5. $4x^2 - 12x + 3 = 0$

6. $x^2 - 2x - 4 = 0$

10-3 Study Guide and Intervention
Solving Quadratic Equations by Completing the Square

Find the Square Root An equation such as $x^2 - 4x + 4 = 5$ can be solved by taking the square root of each side.

Example 1 Solve $x^2 - 2x + 1 = 9$. Round to the nearest tenth if necessary.

$$x^2 - 2x + 1 = 9$$
$$(x - 1)^2 = 9$$
$$\sqrt{(x - 1)^2} = \sqrt{9}$$
$$|x - 1| = \sqrt{9}$$
$$x - 1 = \pm 3$$
$$x - 1 + 1 = \pm 3 + 1$$
$$x = 1 \pm 3$$

$$x = 1 + 3 \quad \text{or} \quad x = 1 - 3$$
$$= 4 \qquad\qquad = -2$$

The solution set is $\{-2, 4\}$.

Example 2 Solve $x^2 - 4x + 4 = 5$. Round to the nearest tenth if necessary.

$$x^2 - 4x + 4 = 5$$
$$(x - 2)^2 = 5$$
$$\sqrt{(x - 2)^2} = \sqrt{5}$$
$$|x - 2| = \sqrt{5}$$
$$x - 2 = \pm\sqrt{5}$$
$$x - 2 + 2 = \pm\sqrt{5} + 2$$
$$x = 2 \pm \sqrt{5}$$

Use a calculator to evaluate each value of x.

$$x = 2 + \sqrt{5} \quad \text{or} \quad x = 2 - \sqrt{5}$$
$$\approx 4.2 \qquad\qquad \approx -0.2$$

The solution set is $\{-0.2, 4.2\}$.

Exercises

Solve each equation by taking the square root of each side. Round to the nearest tenth if necessary.

1. $x^2 + 4x + 4 = 9$

2. $m^2 + 12m + 36 = 1$

3. $r^2 - 6r + 9 = 16$

4. $x^2 - 2x + 1 = 25$

5. $x^2 - 8x + 16 = 5$

6. $x^2 - 10x + 25 = 8$

7. $c^2 - 4c + 4 = 7$

8. $p^2 + 16p + 64 = 3$

9. $x^2 + 8x + 16 = 9$

10. $x^2 + 6x + 9 = 4$

11. $a^2 + 8a + 16 = 10$

12. $y^2 - 12y + 36 = 5$

13. $x^2 + 10x + 25 = 1$

14. $y^2 + 14y + 49 = 6$

15. $m^2 - 8m + 16 = 2$

16. $x^2 + 12x + 36 = 10$

17. $a^2 - 14a + 49 = 3$

18. $y^2 + 8y + 16 = 7$

Lesson 10-3

10-3 Study Guide and Intervention (continued)

Solving Quadratic Equations by Completing the Square

Complete the Square Since few quadratic expressions are perfect square trinomials, the method of **completing the square** can be used to solve some quadratic equations. Use the following steps to complete the square for a quadratic expression of the form $ax^2 + bx$.

Step 1	Find $\frac{b}{2}$.
Step 2	Find $\left(\frac{b}{2}\right)^2$.
Step 3	Add $\left(\frac{b}{2}\right)^2$ to $ax^2 + bx$.

Example **Solve $x^2 + 6x + 3 = 10$ by completing the square.**

$x^2 + 6x + 3 = 10$	Original equation
$x^2 + 6x + 3 - 3 = 10 - 3$	Subtract 3 from each side.
$x^2 + 6x = 7$	Simplify.
$x^2 + 6x + 9 = 7 + 9$	Since $\left(\frac{6}{2}\right)^2 = 9$, add 9 to each side.
$(x + 3)^2 = 16$	Factor $x^2 + 6x + 9$.
$x + 3 = \pm 4$	Take the square root of each side.
$x = -3 \pm 4$	Simplify.

$x = -3 + 4$ or $x = -3 - 4$
$\quad = 1$ $\qquad\qquad = -7$

The solution set is $\{-7, 1\}$.

Exercises

Solve each equation by completing the square. Round to the nearest tenth if necessary.

1. $t^2 - 4t + 3 = 0$ 　　　　**2.** $y^2 + 10y = -9$ 　　　　**3.** $y^2 - 8y - 9 = 0$

4. $x^2 - 6x = 16$ 　　　　**5.** $p^2 - 4p - 5 = 0$ 　　　　**6.** $x^2 - 12x = 9$

7. $c^2 + 8c = 20$ 　　　　**8.** $p^2 = 2p + 1$ 　　　　**9.** $x^2 + 20x + 11 = -8$

10. $x^2 - 1 = 5x$ 　　　　**11.** $a^2 = 22a + 23$ 　　　　**12.** $m^2 - 8m = -7$

13. $x^2 + 10x = 24$ 　　　　**14.** $a^2 - 18a = 19$ 　　　　**15.** $b^2 + 16b = -16$

16. $4x^2 = 24 + 4x$ 　　　　**17.** $2m^2 + 4m + 2 = 8$ 　　　　**18.** $4k^2 = 40k + 44$

10-4 Study Guide and Intervention

Solving Quadratic Equations by Using the Quadratic Formula

Quadratic Formula To solve the standard form of the quadratic equation, $ax^2 + bx + c = 0$, use the **Quadratic Formula**.

Quadratic Formula	the formula $x = \dfrac{-b \pm \sqrt{b^2 - 4ac}}{2a}$ that gives the solutions of $ax^2 + bx + c = 0$, where $a \neq 0$

Example 1 Solve $x^2 + 2x = 3$ by using the Quadratic Formula.

Rewrite the equation in standard form.

$x^2 + 2x = 3$ Original equation
$x^2 + 2x - 3 = 3 - 3$ Subtract 3 from each side.
$x^2 + 2x - 3 = 0$ Simplify.

Now let $a = 1$, $b = 2$, and $c = -3$ in the Quadratic Formula.

$x = \dfrac{-b \pm \sqrt{b^2 - 4ac}}{2a}$

$= \dfrac{-2 \pm \sqrt{(2)^2 - 4(1)(-3)}}{2(1)}$

$= \dfrac{-2 \pm \sqrt{16}}{2}$

$x = \dfrac{-2 + 4}{2}$ or $x = \dfrac{-2 - 4}{2}$

$= 1$ $= -3$

The solution set is $\{-3, 1\}$.

Example 2 Solve $x^2 - 6x - 2 = 0$ by using the Quadratic Formula. Round to the nearest tenth if necessary.

For this equation $a = 1$, $b = -6$, and $c = -2$.

$x = \dfrac{-b \pm \sqrt{b^2 - 4ac}}{2a}$

$= \dfrac{6 \pm \sqrt{(-6)^2 - 4(1)(-2)}}{2(1)}$

$= \dfrac{6 \pm \sqrt{44}}{2}$

$x = \dfrac{6 + \sqrt{44}}{2}$ or $x = \dfrac{6 - \sqrt{44}}{2}$

≈ 6.3 ≈ -0.3

The solution set is $\{-0.3, 6.3\}$.

Exercises

Solve each equation by using the Quadratic Formula. Round to the nearest tenth if necessary.

1. $x^2 - 3x + 2 = 0$ **2.** $m^2 - 8m = -16$ **3.** $16r^2 - 8r = -1$

4. $x^2 + 5x = 6$ **5.** $3x^2 + 2x = 8$ **6.** $8x^2 - 8x - 5 = 0$

7. $-4c^2 + 19c = 21$ **8.** $2p^2 + 6p = 5$ **9.** $48x^2 + 22x - 15 = 0$

10. $8x^2 - 4x = 24$ **11.** $2p^2 + 5p = 8$ **12.** $8y^2 + 9y - 4 = 0$

13. $2x^2 + 9x + 4 = 0$ **14.** $8y^2 + 17y + 2 = 0$

15. $3z^2 + 5z - 2 = 0$ **16.** $-2x^2 + 8x + 4 = 0$

17. $a^2 + 3a = 2$ **18.** $2y^2 - 6y + 4 = 0$

Lesson 10-4

10-4 **Study Guide and Intervention** *(continued)*

Solving Quadratic Equations by Using the Quadratic Formula

The Discriminant In the Quadratic Formula, $x = \dfrac{-b \pm \sqrt{b^2 - 4ac}}{2a}$, the expression under the radical sign, $b^2 - 4ac$, is called the **discriminant**. The discriminant can be used to determine the number of real roots for a quadratic equation.

Case 1: $b^2 - 4ac < 0$	Case 2: $b^2 - 4ac = 0$	Case 3: $b^2 - 4ac > 0$
no real roots	one real root	two real roots

Example State the value of the discriminant for each equation. Then determine the number of real roots.

a. $12x^2 + 5x = 4$

Write the equation in standard form.

$12x^2 + 5x = 4$	Original equation
$12x^2 + 5x - 4 = 4 - 4$	Subtract 4 from each side.
$12x^2 + 5x - 4 = 0$	Simplify.

Now find the discriminant.

$$b^2 - 4ac = (5)^2 - 4(12)(-4)$$
$$= 217$$

Since the discriminant is positive, the equation has two real roots.

b. $2x^2 + 3x = -4$

$2x^2 + 3x = -4$	Original equation
$2x^2 + 3x + 4 = -4 + 4$	Add 4 to each side.
$2x^2 + 3x + 4 = 0$	Simplify.

$$b^2 - 4ac = (3)^2 - 4(2)(4)$$
$$= -23$$

Since the discriminant is negative, the equation has no real roots.

Exercises

State the value of the discriminant for each equation. Then determine the number of real roots of the equation.

1. $3x^2 + 2x - 3 = 0$

2. $3n^2 - 7n - 8 = 0$

3. $2d^2 - 10d - 9 = 0$

4. $4x^2 = x + 4$

5. $3x^2 - 13x = 10$

6. $6x^2 - 10x + 10 = 0$

7. $2k^2 - 20 = -k$

8. $6p^2 = -11p - 40$

9. $9 - 18x + 9x^2 = 0$

10. $12x^2 + 9 = -6x$

11. $9a^2 = 81$

12. $16y^2 + 16y + 4 = 0$

13. $8x^2 + 9x = 2$

14. $4a^2 - 4a + 4 = 3$

15. $3b^2 - 18b = -14$

10-5 **Study Guide and Intervention**

Exponential Functions

Graph Exponential Functions

Exponential Function	a function defined by an equation of the form $y = ax$, where $a > 0$ and $a \neq 1$

You can use values of x to find ordered pairs that satisfy an exponential function. Then you can use the ordered pairs to graph the function.

Example 1 **Graph $y = 3^x$. State the y-intercept.**

x	y
-2	$\frac{1}{9}$
-1	$\frac{1}{3}$
0	1
1	3
2	9

The y-intercept is 1.

Example 2 **Graph $y = \left(\frac{1}{4}\right)^x$. Use the graph to determine the approximate value of $\left(\frac{1}{4}\right)^{-0.5}$.**

x	y
-2	16
-1	4
0	1
1	$\frac{1}{4}$
2	$\frac{1}{16}$

The value of $\left(\frac{1}{4}\right)^{-0.5}$ is about 2.

Exercises

1. Graph $y = 0.3^x$. State the y-intercept. Then use the graph to determine the approximate value of $0.3^{-1.5}$. Use a calculator to confirm the value.

Graph each function. State the y-intercept.

2. $y = 3^x + 1$

3. $y = \left(\frac{1}{3}\right)^x + 1$

4. $y = \left(\frac{1}{2}\right)^x - 2$

Lesson 10-5

10-5 Study Guide and Intervention (continued)

Exponential Functions

Identify Exponential Behavior It is sometimes useful to know if a set of data is exponential. One way to tell is to observe the shape of the graph. Another way is to observe the pattern in the set of data.

Example Determine whether the set of data displays exponential behavior.

x	0	2	4	6	8	10
y	64	32	16	8	4	2

Method 1: Graph the Data

The graph shows rapidly decreasing values of y as x increases. This is characteristic of exponential behavior.

Method 2: Look for a Pattern

The domain values increase by regular intervals of 2, while the range values have a common factor of $\frac{1}{2}$. Since the domain values increase by regular intervals and the range values have a common factor, the data are probably exponential.

Exercises

Determine whether the data in each table display exponential behavior. Explain why or why not.

1.

x	0	1	2	3
y	5	10	15	20

2.

x	0	1	2	3
y	3	9	27	81

3.

x	−1	1	3	5
y	32	16	8	4

4.

x	−1	0	1	2	3
y	3	3	3	3	3

5.

x	−5	0	5	10
y	1	0.5	0.25	0.125

6.

x	0	1	2	3	4
y	$\frac{1}{3}$	$\frac{1}{9}$	$\frac{1}{27}$	$\frac{1}{81}$	$\frac{1}{243}$

10-6 Study Guide and Intervention

Growth and Decay

Exponential Growth Population increases and growth of monetary investments are examples of **exponential growth**. This means that an initial amount increases at a steady rate over time.

Exponential Growth	The general equation for exponential growth is $y = C(1 + r)^t$. • y represents the final amount. • C represents the initial amount. • r represents the rate of change expressed as a decimal. • t represents time.

Example 1 POPULATION The population of Johnson City in 1995 was 25,000. Since then, the population has grown at an average rate of 3.2% each year.

a. Write an equation to represent the population of Johnson City since 1995.

The rate 3.2% can be written as 0.032.

$y = C(1 + r)^t$
$y = 25,000(1 + 0.032)^t$
$y = 25,000(1.032)^t$

b. According to the equation, what will the population of Johnson City be in the year 2005?

In 2005, t will equal 2005 − 1995 or 10.

Substitute 10 for t in the equation from part a.

$y = 25,000(1.032)^{10}$ $t = 10$
$\approx 34,256$

In 2005, the population of Johnson City will be about 34,256.

Example 2 INVESTMENT The Garcias have $12,000 in a savings account. The bank pays 3.5% interest on savings accounts, compounded monthly. Find the balance in 3 years.

The rate 3.5% can be written as 0.035.

The special equation for compound interest is $A = P\left(1 + \dfrac{r}{n}\right)^{nt}$, where A represents the balance, P is the initial amount, r represents the annual rate expressed as a decimal, n represents the number of times the interest is compounded each year, and t represents the number of years the money is invested.

$A = P\left(1 + \dfrac{r}{n}\right)^{nt}$

$A = 12,000\left(1 + \dfrac{0.035}{12}\right)^{36}$

$A \approx 12,000(1.00292)^{36}$

$A \approx 13,328.09$

In three years, the balance of the account will be $13,328.09.

Exercises

1. POPULATION The population of the United States has been increasing at an average annual rate of 0.91%. If the population of the United States was about 284,905,400 in the year 2001, predict the U. S. population in the year 2005. **Source:** U. S. Census Bureau

2. INVESTMENT Determine the amount of an investment of $2500 if it is invested at in interest rate of 5.25% compounded monthly for 4 years.

3. POPULATION It is estimated that the population of the world is increasing at an average annual rate of 1.3%. If the population of the world was about 6,167,007,000 in the year 2001, predict the world population in the year 2010. **Source:** U. S. Census Bureau

4. INVESTMENT Determine the amount of an investment of $100,000 if it is invested at an interest rate of 5.2% compounded quarterly for 12 years.

10-6 Study Guide and Intervention *(continued)*

Growth and Decay

Exponential Decay Radioactive decay and depreciation are examples of **exponential decay**. This means that an initial amount decreases at a steady rate over a period of time.

Exponential Decay	The general equation for exponential decay is $y = C(1 - r)^t$. • y represents the final amount. • C represents the initial amount. • r represents the rate of decay expressed as a decimal. • t represents time.

Example **DEPRECIATION** The original price of a tractor was $45,000. The value of the tractor decreases at a steady rate of 12% per year.

a. Write an equation to represent the value of the tractor since it was purchased.

The rate 12% can be written as 0.12.

$y = C(1 - r)^t$ General equation for exponential decay

$y = 45,000(1 - 0.12)^t$ $C = 45,000$ and $r = 0.12$

$y = 45,000(0.88)^t$ Simplify.

b. What is the value of the tractor in 5 years?

$y = 45,000(0.88)^t$ Equation for decay from part a

$y = 45,000(0.88)^5$ $t = 5$

$y \approx 23,747.94$ Use a calculator.

In 5 years, the tractor will be worth about $23,747.94.

Exercises

1. **POPULATION** The population of Bulgaria has been decreasing at an annual rate of 1.3%. If the population of Bulgaria was about 7,797,000 in the year 2000, predict its population in the year 2010. **Source:** U. S. Census Bureau

2. **DEPRECIATION** Carl Gossell is a machinist. He bought some new machinery for about $125,000. He wants to calculate the value of the machinery over the next 10 years for tax purposes. If the machinery depreciates at the rate of 15% per year, what is the value of the machinery (to the nearest $100) at the end of 10 years?

3. **ARCHAEOLOGY** The *half-life* of a radioactive element is defined as the time that it takes for one-half a quantity of the element to decay. Radioactive Carbon-14 is found in all living organisms and has a half-life of 5730 years. Consider a living organism with an original concentration of Carbon-14 of 100 grams.

   a. If the organism lived 5730 years ago, what is the concentration of Carbon-14 today?

   b. If the organism lived 11,460 years ago, determine the concentration of Carbon-14 today.

4. **DEPRECIATION** A new car costs $32,000. It is expected to depreciate 12% each year for 4 years and then depreciate 8% each year thereafter. Find the value of the car in 6 years.

10-7 Study Guide and Intervention

Geometric Sequences

Geometric Sequences A **geometric sequence** is a sequence in which each term after the nonzero first term is found by multiplying the previous term by a constant called the **common ratio**.

Geometric Sequence	a sequence of numbers of the form a, ar, ar^2, ar^3, ..., where $a \neq 0$, and $r \neq 0$ or 1	**Example:** 1, 2, 4, 8, 16, ...

Example 1 Determine whether each sequence is geometric.

a. 3, 6, 9, 12, 15, ...

In this sequence, each term is found by adding 3 to the previous term. The sequence is arithmetic and not geometric.

b. 1, 4, 16, 64, ...

In this sequence, each term is found by multiplying the previous term by 4. The sequence is geometric.

Example 2 Find the next three terms in each geometric sequence.

a. 8, −4, 2, −1, ...

The common factor is $\frac{-4}{8}$ or $-\frac{1}{2}$. Use this information to find the next three terms.

$(-1)\left(-\frac{1}{2}\right) = \frac{1}{2}$

$\frac{1}{2}\left(-\frac{1}{2}\right) = -\frac{1}{4}$

$\left(-\frac{1}{4}\right)\left(-\frac{1}{2}\right) = \frac{1}{8}$

The next three terms are $\frac{1}{2}$, $-\frac{1}{4}$, and $\frac{1}{8}$.

b. 7, 14, 28, 56, ...

The common ratio is $\frac{14}{7}$ or 2. Use this information to find the next three terms.

$56(2) = 112$
$112(2) = 224$
$224(2) = 448$

The next three terms are 112, 224, 448.

Exercises

Determine whether each sequence is geometric.

1. 2, 4, 6, 8, 10, ...

2. 2, 4, 8, 16, 32, ...

3. −10, −5, −2.5, −1.25, ...

4. 100, 400, 1600, 6400, ...

5. $\frac{1}{2}, \frac{1}{3}, \frac{1}{4}, \frac{1}{5}$, ...

6. $\frac{1}{3}, \frac{1}{9}, \frac{1}{27}, \frac{1}{81}$, ...

Find the next three terms in each geometric sequence.

7. 100, 300, 900, 2700, ...

8. $\frac{1}{2}, \frac{1}{4}, \frac{1}{8}, \frac{1}{16}$, ...

9. 80, 40, 20, 10, ...

Find the nth term of each geometric sequence.

10. $a_1 = 5$, $n = 6$, $r = 3$

11. $a_1 = 3$, $n = 5$, $r = 4$

12. $a_1 = -5$, $n = 7$, $r = -2$

10-7 Study Guide and Intervention *(continued)*

Geometric Sequences

Geometric Means A missing term or terms between two nonconsecutive terms in a geometric sequence are called **geometric means**. In the sequence 10, 20, 40, 80, ..., the geometric mean between 10 and 40 is 20. You can use the formula $a_n = a_1 \cdot r^{n-1}$ to find a geometric mean.

Example Find the geometric mean in the sequence 6, ___, 150.

In the sequence, $a_1 = 6$ and $a_3 = 150$. To find a_2, you must first find r.

$a_n = a_1 \cdot r^{n-1}$ Formula for the *n*th term of a geometric sequence

$a_3 = a_1 \cdot r^{3-1}$ $n = 3$

$150 = 6 \cdot r^2$ $a_3 = 150$ and $a_1 = 6$

$\dfrac{150}{6} = \dfrac{6r^2}{6}$ Divide each side by 6.

$25 = r^2$ Simplify.

$\pm 5 = r$ Take the square root of each side.

If $r = 5$, the geometric mean is 6(5) or 30. If $r = -5$, the geometric mean is 6(-5) or -30. Therefore the geometric mean is 30 or -30.

Exercises

Find the geometric means in each sequence.

1. 4, ___, 16

2. 12, ___, 108

3. -8, ___, -128

4. 180, ___, 20

5. -2, ___, -98

6. 600, ___, 150

7. $\dfrac{1}{4}$, ___, $\dfrac{1}{16}$

8. $\dfrac{1}{2}$, ___, $\dfrac{1}{32}$

9. $-\dfrac{3}{5}$, ___, $-\dfrac{15}{16}$

10. 14, ___, $\dfrac{2}{7}$

11. $\dfrac{5}{8}$, ___, 10

12. $-\dfrac{2}{3}$, ___, -54

13. 2.3, ___, 9.2

14. -137.7, ___, -15.3

15. -5.1, ___, -127.5

16. $\dfrac{3}{8}$, ___, $\dfrac{3}{32}$

17. -15, ___, $-\dfrac{3}{5}$

18. 8, ___, 320,000

NAME _____ DATE _____ PERIOD _____

11-1 Study Guide and Intervention
Simplifying Radical Expressions

Product Property of Square Roots The **Product Property of Square Roots** and prime factorization can be used to simplify expressions involving irrational square roots. When you simplify radical expressions with variables, use absolute value to ensure nonnegative results.

Product Property of Square Roots	For any numbers a and b, where $a \geq 0$ and $b \geq 0$, $\sqrt{ab} = \sqrt{a} \cdot \sqrt{b}$.

Example 1 Simplify $\sqrt{180}$.

$$\begin{aligned} \sqrt{180} &= \sqrt{2 \cdot 2 \cdot 3 \cdot 3 \cdot 5} && \text{Prime factorization of 180} \\ &= \sqrt{2^2} \cdot \sqrt{3^2} \cdot \sqrt{5} && \text{Product Property of Square Roots} \\ &= 2 \cdot 3 \cdot \sqrt{5} && \text{Simplify.} \\ &= 6\sqrt{5} && \text{Simplify.} \end{aligned}$$

Example 2 Simplify $\sqrt{120a^2 \cdot b^5 \cdot c^4}$.

$$\begin{aligned} &\sqrt{120a^2 \cdot b^5 \cdot c^4} \\ &= \sqrt{2^3 \cdot 3 \cdot 5 \cdot a^2 \cdot b^5 \cdot c^4} \\ &= \sqrt{2^2} \cdot \sqrt{2} \cdot \sqrt{3} \cdot \sqrt{5} \cdot \sqrt{a^2} \cdot \sqrt{b^4 \cdot b} \cdot \sqrt{c^4} \\ &= 2 \cdot \sqrt{2} \cdot \sqrt{3} \cdot \sqrt{5} \cdot |a| \cdot b^2 \cdot \sqrt{b} \cdot c^2 \\ &= 2|a|b^2c^2\sqrt{30b} \end{aligned}$$

Exercises

Simplify.

1. $\sqrt{28}$ 2. $\sqrt{68}$ 3. $\sqrt{60}$ 4. $\sqrt{75}$

5. $\sqrt{162}$ 6. $\sqrt{3} \cdot \sqrt{6}$ 7. $\sqrt{2} \cdot \sqrt{5}$ 8. $\sqrt{5} \cdot \sqrt{10}$

9. $\sqrt{4a^2}$ 10. $\sqrt{9x^4}$ 11. $\sqrt{300a^4}$ 12. $\sqrt{128c^6}$

13. $4\sqrt{10} \cdot 3\sqrt{6}$ 14. $\sqrt{3x^2} \cdot 3\sqrt{3x^4}$ 15. $\sqrt{20a^2b^4}$ 16. $\sqrt{100x^3y}$

17. $\sqrt{24a^4b^2}$ 18. $\sqrt{81x^4y^2}$ 19. $\sqrt{150a^2b^2c}$

20. $\sqrt{72a^6b^3c^2}$ 21. $\sqrt{45x^2y^5z^8}$ 22. $\sqrt{98x^4y^6z^2}$

145

11-1 **Study Guide and Intervention** *(continued)*

Simplifying Radical Expressions

Quotient Property of Square Roots A fraction containing radicals is in simplest form if no radicals are left in the denominator. The **Quotient Property of Square Roots** and **rationalizing the denominator** can be used to simplify radical expressions that involve division. When you rationalize the denominator, you multiply the numerator and denominator by a radical expression that gives a rational number in the denominator.

Quotient Property of Square Roots	For any numbers a and b, where $a \geq 0$ and $b \geq 0$, $\sqrt{\dfrac{a}{b}} = \dfrac{\sqrt{a}}{\sqrt{b}}$.

Example Simplify $\sqrt{\dfrac{56}{45}}$.

$$\sqrt{\frac{56}{45}} = \sqrt{\frac{4 \cdot 14}{9 \cdot 5}}$$

$$= \frac{2 \cdot \sqrt{14}}{3 \cdot \sqrt{5}} \qquad \text{Simplify the numerator and denominator.}$$

$$= \frac{2\sqrt{14}}{3\sqrt{5}} \cdot \frac{\sqrt{5}}{\sqrt{5}} \qquad \text{Multiply by } \frac{\sqrt{5}}{\sqrt{5}} \text{ to rationalize the denominator.}$$

$$= \frac{2\sqrt{70}}{15} \qquad \text{Product Property of Square Roots}$$

Exercises

Simplify.

1. $\dfrac{\sqrt{9}}{\sqrt{18}}$

2. $\dfrac{\sqrt{8}}{\sqrt{24}}$

3. $\dfrac{\sqrt{100}}{\sqrt{121}}$

4. $\dfrac{\sqrt{75}}{\sqrt{3}}$

5. $\dfrac{8\sqrt{2}}{2\sqrt{8}}$

6. $\sqrt{\dfrac{2}{5}} \cdot \sqrt{\dfrac{6}{5}}$

7. $\sqrt{\dfrac{3}{4}} \cdot \sqrt{\dfrac{5}{2}}$

8. $\sqrt{\dfrac{5}{7}} \cdot \sqrt{\dfrac{2}{5}}$

9. $\sqrt{\dfrac{3a^2}{10b^6}}$

10. $\sqrt{\dfrac{x^6}{y^4}}$

11. $\sqrt{\dfrac{100a^4}{144b^8}}$

12. $\sqrt{\dfrac{75b^3c^6}{a^2}}$

13. $\dfrac{\sqrt{4}}{3 - \sqrt{5}}$

14. $\dfrac{\sqrt{8}}{2 + \sqrt{3}}$

15. $\dfrac{\sqrt{5}}{2 + \sqrt{5}}$

16. $\dfrac{\sqrt{8}}{2\sqrt{7} + 4\sqrt{10}}$

11-2 Study Guide and Intervention

Operations with Radical Expressions

Add and Subtract Radical Expressions When adding or subtracting radical expressions, use the Associative and Distributive Properties to simplify the expressions. If radical expressions are not in simplest form, simplify them.

Example 1 Simplify $10\sqrt{6} - 5\sqrt{3} + 6\sqrt{3} - 4\sqrt{6}$.

$10\sqrt{6} - 5\sqrt{3} + 6\sqrt{3} - 4\sqrt{6} = (10-4)\sqrt{6} + (-5+6)\sqrt{3}$ Associative and Distributive Properties
$$= 6\sqrt{6} + \sqrt{3}$$ Simplify.

Example 2 Simplify $3\sqrt{12} + 5\sqrt{75}$.

$3\sqrt{12} + 5\sqrt{75} = 3\sqrt{2^2 \cdot 3} + 5\sqrt{5^2 \cdot 3}$ Simplify.
$$= 3 \cdot 2\sqrt{3} + 5 \cdot 5\sqrt{3}$$ Simplify.
$$= 6\sqrt{3} + 25\sqrt{3}$$ Simplify.
$$= 31\sqrt{3}$$ Distributive Property

Exercises

Simplify each expression.

1. $2\sqrt{5} + 4\sqrt{5}$

2. $\sqrt{6} - 4\sqrt{6}$

3. $\sqrt{8} - \sqrt{2}$

4. $3\sqrt{75} + 2\sqrt{5}$

5. $\sqrt{20} + 2\sqrt{5} - 3\sqrt{5}$

6. $2\sqrt{3} + \sqrt{6} - 5\sqrt{3}$

7. $\sqrt{12} + 2\sqrt{3} - 5\sqrt{3}$

8. $3\sqrt{6} + 3\sqrt{2} - \sqrt{50} + \sqrt{24}$

9. $\sqrt{8a} - \sqrt{2a} + 5\sqrt{2a}$

10. $\sqrt{54} + \sqrt{24}$

11. $\sqrt{3} + \sqrt{\frac{1}{3}}$

12. $\sqrt{12} + \sqrt{\frac{1}{3}}$

13. $\sqrt{54} - \sqrt{\frac{1}{6}}$

14. $\sqrt{80} - \sqrt{20} + \sqrt{180}$

15. $\sqrt{50} + \sqrt{18} - \sqrt{75} + \sqrt{27}$

16. $2\sqrt{3} - 4\sqrt{45} + 2\sqrt{\frac{1}{3}}$

17. $\sqrt{125} - 2\sqrt{\frac{1}{5}} + \sqrt{\frac{1}{3}}$

18. $\sqrt{\frac{2}{3}} + 3\sqrt{3} - 4\sqrt{\frac{1}{12}}$

Lesson 11-2

11-2 Study Guide and Intervention (continued)

Operations with Radical Expressions

Multiply Radical Expressions Multiplying two radical expressions with different radicands is similar to multiplying binomials.

Example Multiply $(3\sqrt{2} - 2\sqrt{5})(4\sqrt{20} + \sqrt{8})$.

Use the FOIL method.

$(3\sqrt{2} - 2\sqrt{5})(4\sqrt{20} + \sqrt{8}) = (3\sqrt{2})(4\sqrt{20}) + (3\sqrt{2})(\sqrt{8}) + (-2\sqrt{5})(4\sqrt{20}) + (-2\sqrt{5})(\sqrt{8})$

$= 12\sqrt{40} + 3\sqrt{16} - 8\sqrt{100} - 2\sqrt{40}$ Multiply.

$= 12\sqrt{2^2 \cdot 10} + 3 \cdot 4 - 8 \cdot 10 - 2\sqrt{2^2 \cdot 10}$ Simplify.

$= 24\sqrt{10} + 12 - 80 - 4\sqrt{10}$ Simplify.

$= 20\sqrt{10} - 68$ Combine like terms.

Exercises

Find each product.

1. $2(\sqrt{3} + 4\sqrt{5})$

2. $\sqrt{6}(\sqrt{3} - 2\sqrt{6})$

3. $\sqrt{5}(\sqrt{5} - \sqrt{2})$

4. $\sqrt{2}(3\sqrt{7} + 2\sqrt{5})$

5. $(2 - 4\sqrt{2})(2 + 4\sqrt{2})$

6. $(3 + \sqrt{6})^2$

7. $(2 - 2\sqrt{5})^2$

8. $3\sqrt{2}(\sqrt{8} + \sqrt{24})$

9. $\sqrt{8}(\sqrt{2} + 5\sqrt{8})$

10. $(\sqrt{5} - 3\sqrt{2})(\sqrt{5} + 3\sqrt{2})$

11. $(\sqrt{3} + \sqrt{6})^2$

12. $(\sqrt{2} - 2\sqrt{3})^2$

13. $(\sqrt{5} - \sqrt{2})(\sqrt{2} + \sqrt{6})$

14. $(\sqrt{8} - \sqrt{2})(\sqrt{3} + \sqrt{6})$

15. $(\sqrt{5} - \sqrt{18})(7\sqrt{5} + \sqrt{3})$

16. $(2\sqrt{3} - \sqrt{45})(\sqrt{12} + 2\sqrt{6})$

17. $(2\sqrt{5} - 2\sqrt{3})(\sqrt{10} + \sqrt{6})$

18. $(\sqrt{2} + 3\sqrt{3})(\sqrt{12} - 4\sqrt{8})$

DATE _____ PERIOD _____

11-3 Study Guide and Intervention

Radical Equations

Radical Equations Equations containing radicals with variables in the radicand are
called **radical equations**. These can be solved by first using the following steps.

Step 1	Isolate the radical on one side of the equation.
Step 2	Square each side of the equation to eliminate the radical.

Example 1 Solve $16 = \frac{\sqrt{x}}{2}$ for x.

$16 = \frac{\sqrt{x}}{2}$ Original equation

$2(16) = 2\left(\frac{\sqrt{x}}{2}\right)$ Multiply each side by 2.

$32 = \sqrt{x}$ Simplify.

$(32)^2 = (\sqrt{x})^2$ Square each side.

$1024 = x$ Simplify.

The solution is 1024, which checks in the
original equation.

Example 2 Solve $\sqrt{4x - 7} + 2 = 7$.

$\sqrt{4x - 7} + 2 = 7$ Original equation

$\sqrt{4x - 7} + 2 - 2 = 7 - 2$ Subtract 2 from each side.

$\sqrt{4x - 7} = 5$ Simplify.

$(\sqrt{4x - 7})^2 = 5^2$ Square each side.

$4x - 7 = 25$ Simplify.

$4x - 7 + 7 = 25 + 7$ Add 7 to each side.

$4x = 32$ Simplify.

$x = 8$ Divide each side by 4.

The solution is 8, which checks in the original
equation.

Exercises

Solve each equation. Check your solution.

1. $\sqrt{a} = 8$

2. $\sqrt{a} + 6 = 32$

3. $2\sqrt{x} = 8$

4. $7 = \sqrt{26 - n}$

5. $\sqrt{-a} = 6$

6. $\sqrt{3r^2} = 3$

7. $2\sqrt{3} = \sqrt{y}$

8. $2\sqrt{3a} - 2 = 7$

9. $\sqrt{x - 4} = 6$

10. $\sqrt{2c + 3} = 5$

11. $\sqrt{3b - 2} + 19 = 24$

12. $\sqrt{4x - 1} = 3$

13. $\sqrt{3r + 2} = 2\sqrt{3}$

14. $\sqrt{\frac{x}{2}} = \frac{1}{2}$

15. $\sqrt{\frac{x}{8}} = 4$

16. $\sqrt{6x^2 + 5x} = 2$

17. $\sqrt{\frac{x}{3}} + 6 = 8$

18. $2\sqrt{\frac{3x}{5}} + 3 = 11$

© Glencoe/McGraw-Hill   **149**   *Glencoe Algebra 1*

11-3 Study Guide and Intervention (continued)

Radical Equations

Extraneous Solutions To solve a radical equation with a variable on both sides, you need to square each side of the equation. Squaring each side of an equation sometimes produces **extraneous solutions**, or solutions that are not solutions of the original equation. Therefore, it is very important that you check each solution.

Example **Solve $\sqrt{x + 3} = x - 3$.**

$\sqrt{x + 3} = x - 3$	Original equation
$(\sqrt{x + 3})^2 = (x - 3)^2$	Square each side.
$x + 3 = x^2 - 6x + 9$	Simplify.
$0 = x^2 - 7x + 6$	Subtract x and 3 from each side.
$0 = (x - 1)(x - 6)$	Factor.
$x - 1 = 0$ or $x - 6 = 0$	Zero Product Property
$x = 1$ $x = 6$	Solve.

CHECK
$\sqrt{x + 3} = x - 3$ $\sqrt{x + 3} = x - 3$
$\sqrt{1 + 3} \overset{?}{=} 1 - 3$ $\sqrt{6 + 3} \overset{?}{=} 6 - 3$
$\sqrt{4} \overset{?}{=} -2$ $\sqrt{9} \overset{?}{=} 3$
$2 \neq -2$ $3 = 3$ ✓

Since $x = 1$ does not satisfy the original equation, $x = 6$ is the only solution.

Exercises

Solve each equation. Check your solution.

1. $\sqrt{a} = a$

2. $\sqrt{a + 6} = a$

3. $2\sqrt{x} = x$

4. $n = \sqrt{2 - n}$

5. $\sqrt{-a} = a$

6. $\sqrt{10 - 6k} + 3 = k$

7. $\sqrt{y - 1} = y - 1$

8. $\sqrt{3a - 2} = a$

9. $\sqrt{x + 2} = x$

10. $\sqrt{2c + 5} = c - 5$

11. $\sqrt{3b + 6} = b + 2$

12. $\sqrt{4x - 4} = x$

13. $r + \sqrt{2 - r} = 2$

14. $\sqrt{x^2 + 10x} = x + 4$

15. $-2\sqrt{\dfrac{x}{8}} = 15$

16. $\sqrt{6x^2 - 4x} = x + 2$

17. $\sqrt{2y^2 - 64} = y$

18. $\sqrt{3x^2 + 12x + 1} = x + 5$

11-4 Study Guide and Intervention

The Pythagorean Theorem

The Pythagorean Theorem The side opposite the right angle in a right triangle is called the **hypotenuse**. This side is always the longest side of a right triangle. The other two sides are called the **legs** of the triangle. To find the length of any side of a right triangle, given the lengths of the other two sides, you can use the **Pythagorean Theorem**.

Pythagorean Theorem	If a and b are the measures of the legs of a right triangle and c is the measure of the hypotenuse, then $c^2 = a^2 + b^2$.	

Example 1 Find the length of the hypotenuse of a right triangle if $a = 5$ and $b = 12$.

$c^2 = a^2 + b^2$ Pythagorean Theorem

$c^2 = 5^2 + 12^2$ $a = 5$ and $b = 12$

$c^2 = 169$ Simplify.

$c = \sqrt{169}$ Take the square root of each side.

$c = 13$

The length of the hypotenuse is 13.

Example 2 Find the length of a leg of a right triangle if $a = 8$ and $c = 10$.

$c^2 = a^2 + b^2$ Pythagorean Theorem

$10^2 = 8^2 + b^2$ $a = 8$ and $c = 10$

$100 = 64 + b^2$ Simplify.

$36 = b^2$ Subtract 64 from each side.

$b = \pm\sqrt{36}$ Take the square root of each side.

$b = \pm 6$

The length of the leg is 6.

Exercises

Find the length of each missing side. If necessary, round to the nearest hundredth.

1.

2.

3.

If c is the measure of the hypotenuse of a right triangle, find each missing measure. If necessary, round to the nearest hundredth.

4. $a = 10, b = 12, c = ?$

5. $a = 9, b = 12, c = ?$

6. $a = 12, b = ?, c = 16$

7. $a = ?, b = 6, c = 8$

8. $a = ?, b = \sqrt{8}, c = \sqrt{18}$

9. $a = \sqrt{5}, b = \sqrt{10}, c = ?$

Lesson 11-4

11-4 Study Guide and Intervention (continued)

The Pythagorean Theorem

Right Triangles If a and b are the measures of the shorter sides of a triangle, c is the measure of the longest side, and $c^2 = a^2 + b^2$, then the triangle is a right triangle.

Example Determine whether the following side measures form right triangles.

a. 10, 12, 14

Since the measure of the longest side is 14, let $c = 14$, $a = 10$, and $b = 12$.

$c^2 = a^2 + b^2$ Pythagorean Theorem

$14^2 \overset{?}{=} 10^2 + 12^2$ $a = 10$, $b = 12$, $c = 14$

$196 \overset{?}{=} 100 + 144$ Multiply.

$196 \neq 244$ Add.

Since $c^2 \neq a^2 + b^2$, the triangle is not a right triangle.

b. 7, 24, 25

Since the measure of the longest side is 25, let $c = 25$, $a = 7$, and $b = 24$.

$c^2 = a^2 + b^2$ Pythagorean Theorem

$25^2 \overset{?}{=} 7^2 + 24^2$ $a = 7$, $b = 24$, $c = 25$

$625 \overset{?}{=} 49 + 576$ Multiply.

$625 = 625$ Add.

Since $c^2 = a^2 + b^2$, the triangle is a right triangle.

Exercises

Determine whether the following side measures form right triangles.

1. 14, 48, 50   **2.** 6, 8, 10   **3.** 8, 8, 10

4. 90, 120, 150   **5.** 15, 20, 25   **6.** 4, 8, $4\sqrt{5}$

7. 2, 2, $\sqrt{8}$ **8.** 4, 4, $\sqrt{20}$ **9.** 25, 30, 35

10. 24, 36, 48   **11.** 18, 80, 82   **12.** 150, 200, 250

13. 100, 200, 300   **14.** 500, 1200, 1300   **15.** 700, 1000, 1300

11-5 Study Guide and Intervention

The Distance Formula

The Distance Formula The Pythagorean Theorem can be used to derive the **Distance Formula** shown below. The Distance Formula can then be used to find the distance between any two points in the coordinate plane.

Distance Formula	The distance between any two points with coordinates (x_1, y_1) and (x_2, y_2) is given by $d = \sqrt{(x_2 - x_1)^2 + (y_2 - y_1)^2}$.

Example 1 Find the distance between the points at $(-5, 2)$ and $(4, 5)$.

$d = \sqrt{(x_2 - x_1)^2 + (y_2 - y_1)^2}$ Distance Formula

$= \sqrt{(4 - (-5))^2 + (5 - 2)^2}$ $(x_1, y_1) = (-5, 2), (x_2, y_2) = (4, 5)$

$= \sqrt{9^2 + 3^2}$ Simplify.

$= \sqrt{81 + 9}$ Evaluate squares and simplify.

$= \sqrt{90}$

The distance is $\sqrt{90}$, or about 9.49 units.

Example 2 Jill draws a line segment from point $(1, 4)$ on her computer screen to point $(98, 49)$. How long is the segment?

$d = \sqrt{(x_2 - x_1)^2 + (y_2 - y_1)^2}$

$= \sqrt{(98 - 1)^2 + (49 - 4)^2}$

$= \sqrt{97^2 + 45^2}$

$= \sqrt{9409 + 2025}$

$= \sqrt{11,434}$

The segment is about 106.93 units long.

Exercises

Find the distance between each pair of points whose coordinates are given. Express answers in simplest radical form and as decimal approximations rounded to the nearest hundredth if necessary.

1. $(1, 5), (3, 1)$

2. $(0, 0), (6, 8)$

3. $(-2, -8), (7, -3)$

4. $(6, -7), (-2, 8)$

5. $(1, 5), (-8, 4)$

6. $(3, -4), (-4, -4)$

7. $(-1, 4), (3, 2)$

8. $(0, 0), (-3, 5)$

9. $(2, -6), (-7, 1)$

10. $(-2, -5), (0, 8)$

11. $(3, 4), (0, 0)$

12. $(3, -4), (-4, -16)$

13. $(1, -1), (3, -2)$

14. $(-2, 0), (-3, -9)$

15. $(-9, 0), (-2, 5)$

16. $(2, -7), (-2, -2)$

17. $(1, -3), (-8, 21)$

18. $(-3, -5), (1, -8)$

Lesson 11-5

11-5 Study Guide and Intervention *(continued)*

The Distance Formula

Find Coordinates If you know the coordinates of one point and only one coordinate of a second point, you can use the Distance Formula to find the missing coordinate of the second point.

Example **Find the value of a if the distance between the points at $(-3, -2)$ and $(a, -5)$ is 5 units.**

$d = \sqrt{(x_2 - x_1)^2 + (y_2 - y_1)^2}$	Distance Formula
$5 = \sqrt{(a - (-3))^2 + (-5 - (-2))^2}$	$(x_1, y_1) = (-3, -2), (x_2, y_2) = (a, -5)$, and $d = 5$
$5 = \sqrt{(a + 3)^2 + (-3)^2}$	Simplify.
$5 = \sqrt{a^2 + 6a + 9 + 9}$	Evaluate squares.
$5 = \sqrt{a^2 + 6a + 18}$	Simplify.
$5^2 = \left(\sqrt{a^2 + 6a + 18}\right)^2$	Square each side.
$25 = a^2 + 6a + 18$	Simplify.
$0 = a^2 + 6a - 7$	Subtract 25 from each side.
$0 = (a + 7)(a - 1)$	Factor.
$a + 7 = 0$ or $a - 1 = 0$	Zero Product Property
$a = -7 \qquad\qquad a = 1$	

The value of a is -7 or 1.

Exercises

Find the possible values of a if the points with the given coordinates are the indicated distance apart.

1. $(1, a), (3, -2); d = \sqrt{5}$

2. $(0, 0), (a, 4); d = 5$

3. $(2, -1), (a, 3); d = 5$

4. $(1, -3), (a, 21); d = 25$

5. $(1, a), (-2, 4); d = 3$

6. $(3, -4), (-4, a); d = \sqrt{65}$

7. $(a, -4), (-3, -2); d = \sqrt{13}$

8. $(0, 3), (3, a); d = 3\sqrt{2}$

9. $(a, 3), (2, -4); d = \sqrt{74}$

10. $(-2, -5), (a, -2); d = 5$

11. $(3, 3), (-1, a); d = 5$

12. $(-1, -1), (4, a); d = \sqrt{41}$

13. $(a, 5), (-1, 2); d = \sqrt{45}$

14. $(4, -2), (a, 0); d = 2\sqrt{2}$

15. $(-2, 1), (a, -3); d = 2\sqrt{5}$

11-6 Study Guide and Intervention

Similar Triangles

Lesson 11-6

Similar Triangles $\triangle RST$ is **similar** to $\triangle XYZ$. The angles of the two triangles have equal measure. They are called **corresponding angles**. The sides opposite the corresponding angles are called **corresponding sides**.

Similar Triangles	If two triangles are similar, then the measures of their corresponding sides are proportional and the measures of their corresponding angles are equal.	$\triangle ABC \sim \triangle DEF$ $\dfrac{AB}{DE} = \dfrac{BC}{EF} = \dfrac{AC}{DF}$	

Example 1 Determine whether the pair of triangles is similar. Justify your answer.

Since corresponding angles do not have the equal measures, the triangles are not similar.

Example 2 Determine whether the pair of triangles is similar. Justify your answer.

The measure of $\angle G = 180° - (90° + 45°) = 45°$.
The measure of $\angle I = 180° - (45° + 45°) = 90°$.
Since corresponding angles have equal measures, $\triangle EFG \sim \triangle HIJ$.

Exercises

Determine whether each pair of triangles is similar. Justify your answer.

1.

2.

3.

4.

5.

6.

11-6 Study Guide and Intervention *(continued)*

Similar Triangles

Find Unknown Measures If some of the measurements are known, proportions can be used to find the measures of the other sides of similar triangles.

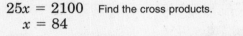

Example INDIRECT MEASUREMENT

△ABC ~ △AED **in the figure at the right. Find the height of the apartment building.**

Let $BC = x$.

$$\frac{ED}{BC} = \frac{AD}{AC}$$

$$\frac{7}{x} = \frac{25}{300} \qquad ED = 7, AD = 25, AC = 300$$

$25x = 2100$ Find the cross products.

$x = 84$

The apartment building is 84 meters high.

Exercises

For each set of measures, find the measures of the missing sides if △ABC ~ △DEF.

1. $c = 15, d = 8, e = 6, f = 10$

2. $c = 20, a = 12, b = 8, f = 15$

3. $a = 8, d = 8, e = 6, f = 7$

4. $a = 20, d = 10, e = 8, f = 10$

5. $c = 5, d = 10, e = 8, f = 8$

6. $a = 25, b = 20, c = 15, f = 12$

7. $b = 8, d = 8, e = 4, f = 10$

8. INDIRECT MEASUREMENT Bruce likes to amuse his brother by shining a flashlight on his hand and making a shadow on the wall. How far is it from the flashlight to the wall?

9. INDIRECT MEASUREMENT A forest ranger uses similar triangles to find the height of a tree. Find the height of the tree.

11-7 Study Guide and Intervention

Trigonometric Ratios

Trigonometric Ratios For each acute angle of a right triangle, certain ratios of side lengths are useful. These ratios are called **trigonometric ratios**. Three common ratios are the **sine**, **cosine**, and **tangent**, as defined at the right.

sine of $\angle A$	$\sin A = \dfrac{a}{c}$
cosine of $\angle A$	$\cos A = \dfrac{b}{c}$
tangent of $\angle A$	$\tan A = \dfrac{a}{b}$

Example

a. Find the sine, cosine, and tangent of $\angle R$ of $\triangle RST$. Round to the nearest thousandth.

$\sin R = \dfrac{2\sqrt{19}}{20} \approx 0.436$ $r = 2\sqrt{19}, s = 20$

$\cos R = \dfrac{18}{20} = 0.9$ $t = 18, s = 20$

$\tan R = \dfrac{2\sqrt{19}}{18} \approx 0.484$ $r = 2\sqrt{19}, t = 18$

b. Find the measure of $\angle R$ to the nearest degree.

$\tan R \approx 0.484$ From part a above

Use TAN⁻¹ on a calculator to find the measure of the angle whose tangent ratio is 0.484.
KEYSTROKES: [2nd] [TAN⁻¹] .484 [ENTER] 25.82698212 or about 26°

Exercises

Find the sine, cosine, and tangent of each acute angle. Round your answers to the nearest ten thousandth.

1.

2.

Use a calculator to find the value of each trigonometric ratio to the nearest ten thousandth.

3. $\sin 45°$

4. $\cos 47°$

5. $\tan 48°$

Use a calculator to find the measure of each angle to the nearest degree.

6. $\sin A = 0.7547$

7. $\tan C = 2.3456$

8. $\cos B = 0.6947$

9. $\sin A = 0.6589$

10. $\tan C = 1.9832$

11. $\cos B = 0.0136$

Lesson 11-7

11-7 Study Guide and Intervention *(continued)*

Trigonometric Ratios

Solve Triangles Finding the measures of all angles and sides in a right triangle is called **solving the triangle**. You can use trigonometric ratios or the Pythagorean Theorem to find missing side measures.

Example **Find all of the missing measures in △ABC.**

Step 1 Since the sum of the measures of the angles of a triangle is 180°, $m\angle B = 180° - 90° - 48° = 42°$.

Step 2 Find the value of x.

$\sin 48° = \dfrac{x}{10}$ Definition of sine

$0.7431 \approx \dfrac{x}{10}$ Evaluate sin 48°.

$7.4 \approx x$ Multiply by 10.

Step 3 Find the value of y.

$\cos 48° = \dfrac{y}{10}$ Definition of cosine

$0.6691 \approx \dfrac{y}{10}$ Evaluate cos 48°.

$6.7 \approx y$ Multiply by 10.

So the missing measures are 42°, 7.4 in., and 6.7 in.

Exercises

Solve each triangle. State the side lengths to the nearest tenth and the angle measures to the nearest degree.

1.

2.

3.

4.

5.

6.

12-1 Study Guide and Intervention

Inverse Variation

Graph Inverse Variation Situations in which the values of y decrease as the values of x increase are examples of **inverse variation**. We say that y varies inversely as x, or y is inversely proportional to x.

Inverse Variation Equation	an equation of the form $xy = k$, where $k \neq 0$

Example 1 Suppose you drive 200 miles without stopping. The time it takes to travel a distance varies inversely as the rate at which you travel. Let x = speed in miles per hour and y = time in hours. Graph the variation.

The equation $xy = 200$ can be used to represent the situation. Use various speeds to make a table.

x	y
10	20
20	10
30	6.7
40	5
50	4
60	3.3

Example 2 Graph an inverse variation in which y varies inversely as x and $y = 3$ when $x = 12$.

Solve for k.

$xy = k$ Inverse variation equation
$12(3) = k$ $x = 12$ and $y = 3$
$36 = k$ Simplify.

Choose values for x and y whose product is 36.

x	y
−6	−6
−3	−12
−2	−18
2	18
3	12
6	6

Exercises

Graph each variation if y varies inversely as x.

1. $y = 9$ when $x = -3$

2. $y = 12$ when $x = 4$

3. $y = -25$ when $x = 5$

4. $y = 4$ when $x = 5$

5. $y = -18$ when $x = -9$

6. $y = 4.8$ when $x = 5.4$

Lesson 12-1

12-1 Study Guide and Intervention (continued)

Inverse Variation

Use Inverse Variation If two points (x_1, y_1) and (x_2, y_2) are solutions of an inverse variation, then $x_1 \cdot y_1 = k$ and $x_2 \cdot y_2 = k$.

Product Rule or Inverse Variation	the equation $x_1 \cdot y_1 = x_2 \cdot y_2$

From the product rule, you can form the proportion $\dfrac{x_1}{x_2} = \dfrac{y_2}{y_1}$.

Example **If y varies inversely as x and $y = 12$ when $x = 4$, find x when $y = 18$.**

Method 1 Use the product rule.

$x_1 \cdot y_1 = x_2 \cdot y_2$ Product rule for inverse variation

$4 \cdot 12 = x_2 \cdot 18$ $x_1 = 4, y_1 = 12, y_2 = 18$

$\dfrac{48}{18} = x_2$ Divide each side by 18.

$\dfrac{8}{3} = x_2$ Simplify.

Method 2 Use a proportion.

$\dfrac{x_1}{x_2} = \dfrac{y_2}{y_1}$ Proportion for inverse variation

$\dfrac{4}{x_2} = \dfrac{18}{12}$ $x_1 = 4, y_1 = 12, y_2 = 18$

$48 = 18x_2$ Cross multiply.

$\dfrac{8}{3} = x_2$ Simplify.

Both methods show that $x_2 = \dfrac{8}{3}$ when $y = 18$.

Exercises

Write an inverse variation equation that relates x and y. Assume that y varies inversely as x. Then solve.

1. If $y = 10$ when $x = 5$, find y when $x = 2$.

2. If $y = 8$ when $x = -2$, find y when $x = 4$.

3. If $y = 70$ when $x = 7$, find y when $x = -5$.

4. If $y = 1.5$ when $x = 0.5$, find x when $y = 3$.

5. If $y = 100$ when $x = 120$, find x when $y = 20$.

6. If $y = -16$ when $x = 4$, find x when $y = 32$.

7. If $y = -7.5$ when $x = 25$, find y when $x = 5$.

8. If $y = \dfrac{1}{2}$ when $x = \dfrac{1}{8}$, find y when $x = \dfrac{1}{2}$.

9. If $y = \dfrac{3}{4}$ when $x = \dfrac{5}{4}$, find y when $x = \dfrac{1}{2}$.

10. DRIVING The Gerardi family can travel to Oshkosh, Wisconsin, from Chicago, Illinois, in 4 hours if they drive an average of 45 miles per hour. How long would it take them if they increased their average speed to 50 miles per hour?

11. GEOMETRY For a rectangle with given area, the width of the rectangle varies inversely as the length. If the width of the rectangle is 40 meters when the length is 5 meters, find the width of the rectangle when the length is 20 meters.

12-2 Study Guide and Intervention

Rational Expressions

Excluded Values of Rational Expressions

Rational Expression	an algebraic fraction whose numerator and denominator are polynomials	Example: $\dfrac{x^2 + 1}{y^2}$

Because a rational expression involves division, the denominator cannot equal zero. Any value of the denominator that results in division by zero is called an **excluded value** of the denominator.

Example 1 State the excluded value of $\dfrac{4m - 8}{m + 2}$.

Exclude the values for which $m + 2 = 0$.

$m + 2 = 0$ The denominator cannot equal 0.

$m + 2 - 2 = 0 - 2$ Subtract 2 from each side.

$m = -2$ Simplify.

Therefore, m cannot equal -2.

Example 2 State the excluded values of $\dfrac{x^2 + 1}{x^2 - 9}$.

Exclude the values for which $x^2 - 9 = 0$.

$x^2 - 9 = 0$ The denominator cannot equal 0.

$(x + 3)(x - 3) = 0$ Factor.

$x + 3 = 0$ or $x - 3 = 0$ Zero Product Property

$= -3$ $= 3$

Therefore, x cannot equal -3 or 3.

Exercises

State the excluded values for each rational expression.

1. $\dfrac{2b}{b - 8}$

2. $\dfrac{12 - a}{32 + a}$

3. $\dfrac{x^2 - 2}{x + 4}$

4. $\dfrac{m^2 - 4}{2m + 8}$

5. $\dfrac{2n - 12}{n^2 - 4}$

6. $\dfrac{2x + 18}{x^2 - 16}$

7. $\dfrac{x^2 - 4}{x^2 + 4x + 4}$

8. $\dfrac{a - 1}{a^2 + 5a + 6}$

9. $\dfrac{k^2 - 2k + 1}{k^2 + 4k + 3}$

10. $\dfrac{m^2 - 1}{2m^2 - m - 1}$

11. $\dfrac{25 - n^2}{n^2 - 4n - 5}$

12. $\dfrac{2x^2 + 5x + 1}{x^2 - 10x + 16}$

13. $\dfrac{n^2 - 2n - 3}{n^2 + 4n - 5}$

14. $\dfrac{y^2 - y - 2}{3y^2 - 12}$

15. $\dfrac{k^2 + 2k - 3}{k^2 - 20k + 64}$

16. $\dfrac{x^2 + 4x + 4}{4x^2 + 11x - 3}$

Lesson 12-2

12-2 Study Guide and Intervention *(continued)*

Rational Expressions

Simplify Rational Expressions Factoring polynomials is a useful tool for simplifying rational expressions. To simplify a rational expression, first factor the numerator and denominator. Then divide each by the greatest common factor.

Example 1 Simplify $\dfrac{54z^3}{24yz}$.

$\dfrac{54z^3}{24yz} = \dfrac{(6z)(9z^2)}{(6z)(4y)}$ The GCF of the numerator and the denominator is 6z.

$= \dfrac{\overset{1}{\cancel{(6z)}}(9z^2)}{1\,\cancel{(6z)}(4y)}$ Divide the numerator and denominator by 6z.

$= \dfrac{9z^2}{4y}$ Simplify.

Example 2 Simplify $\dfrac{3x - 9}{x^2 - 5x + 6}$. **State the excluded values of x.**

$\dfrac{3x - 9}{x^2 - 5x + 6} = \dfrac{3(x - 3)}{(x - 2)(x - 3)}$ Factor.

$= \dfrac{3\overset{1}{\cancel{(x - 3)}}}{(x - 2)\cancel{(x - 3)}_1}$ Divide by the GCF, $x - 3$.

$= \dfrac{3}{x - 2}$ Simplify.

Exclude the values for which $x^2 - 5x + 6 = 0$.

$x^2 - 5x + 6 = 0$
$(x - 2)(x - 3) = 0$
$x = 2$ or $x = 3$
Therefore, $x \neq 2$ and $x \neq 3$.

Exercises

Simplify each expression. State the excluded values of the variables.

1. $\dfrac{12ab}{a^2b^2}$

2. $\dfrac{7n^3}{21n^8}$

3. $\dfrac{x + 2}{x^2 - 4}$

4. $\dfrac{m^2 - 4}{m^2 + 6m + 8}$

5. $\dfrac{2n - 8}{n^2 - 16}$

6. $\dfrac{x^2 + 2x + 1}{x^2 - 1}$

7. $\dfrac{x^2 - 4}{x^2 + 4x + 4}$

8. $\dfrac{a^2 + 3a + 2}{a^2 + 5a + 6}$

9. $\dfrac{k^2 - 1}{k^2 + 4k + 3}$

10. $\dfrac{m^2 - 2m + 1}{2m^2 - m - 1}$

11. $\dfrac{n^2 - 25}{n^2 - 4n - 5}$

12. $\dfrac{x^2 + x - 6}{2x^2 - 8}$

13. $\dfrac{n^2 + 7n + 12}{n^2 + 2n - 8}$

14. $\dfrac{y^2 - y - 2}{y^2 - 10y + 16}$

12-3 Study Guide and Intervention

Multiplying Rational Expressions

Multiply Rational Expressions To multiply rational expressions, you multiply the numerators and multiply the denominators. Then simplify.

Example 1 Find $\dfrac{2c^2d}{5ab^2} \cdot \dfrac{a^2b}{3cd}$.

$$\dfrac{2c^2d}{5ab^2} \cdot \dfrac{a^2b}{3cd} = \dfrac{2a^2bc^2d}{15ab^2cd} \qquad \text{Multiply.}$$

$$= \dfrac{{}^1(abcd)(2ac)}{{}_1(abcd)(15b)} \qquad \text{Simplify.}$$

$$= \dfrac{2ac}{15b} \qquad \text{Simplify.}$$

Example 2 Find $\dfrac{x^2 - 16}{2x + 8} \cdot \dfrac{x + 4}{x^2 + 8x + 16}$.

$$\dfrac{x^2 - 16}{2x + 8} \cdot \dfrac{x + 4}{x^2 + 8x + 16} = \dfrac{(x - 4)(x + 4)}{2(x + 4)} \cdot \dfrac{x + 4}{(x + 4)(x + 4)} \qquad \text{Factor.}$$

$$= \dfrac{(x - 4)\cancel{(x + 4)}^{\,1}}{2\cancel{(x + 4)}_{\,1}} \cdot \dfrac{\cancel{x + 4}^{\,1}}{(x + 4)\cancel{(x + 4)}_{\,1}} \qquad \text{Simplify.}$$

$$= \dfrac{x - 4}{2x + 8} \qquad \text{Multiply.}$$

Exercises

Find each product.

1. $\dfrac{6ab}{a^2b^2} \cdot \dfrac{a^2}{b^2}$

2. $\dfrac{mn^2}{3} \cdot \dfrac{4}{mn}$

3. $\dfrac{x + 2}{x - 4} \cdot \dfrac{x - 4}{x - 1}$

4. $\dfrac{m - 5}{8} \cdot \dfrac{16}{m - 5}$

5. $\dfrac{2n - 8}{n + 2} \cdot \dfrac{2n + 4}{n - 4}$

6. $\dfrac{x^2 - 16}{2x + 8} \cdot \dfrac{x + 4}{x^2 + 8x + 16}$

7. $\dfrac{8x + 8}{x^2 - 2x + 1} \cdot \dfrac{x - 1}{2x + 2}$

8. $\dfrac{a^2 - 25}{a + 2} \cdot \dfrac{a^2 - 4}{a - 5}$

9. $\dfrac{x^2 + 6x + 8}{2x^2 + 9x + 4} \cdot \dfrac{2x^2 - x - 1}{x^2 - 3x + 2}$

10. $\dfrac{m^2 - 1}{2m^2 - m - 1} \cdot \dfrac{2m + 1}{m^2 - 2m + 1}$

11. $\dfrac{n^2 - 1}{n^2 - 7n + 10} \cdot \dfrac{n^2 - 25}{n^2 + 6n + 5}$

12. $\dfrac{3p - 3q}{10pq} \cdot \dfrac{20p^2q^2}{p^2 - q^2}$

13. $\dfrac{a^2 + 7a + 12}{a^2 + 2a - 8} \cdot \dfrac{a^2 + 3a - 10}{a^2 + 2a - 8}$

14. $\dfrac{v^2 - 4v - 21}{3v^2 + 6v} \cdot \dfrac{v^2 + 8v}{v^2 + 11v + 24}$

Lesson 12-3

12-3 Study Guide and Intervention *(continued)*

Multiplying Rational Expressions

Dimensional Analysis Multiplying fractions that involve units of measure can be simplified by dividing units of measure. This is similar to simplifying rational expressions by dividing out common factors.

Example The tank of a car holds 15 gallons of gasoline. You want to travel 1200 miles on a vacation. If the car averages 24 miles per gallon, how many tanks of gasoline can you expect to use for this trip?

$$\frac{1200 \text{ miles}}{1 \text{ trip}} \cdot \frac{1 \text{ gallon}}{24 \text{ miles}} \cdot \frac{1 \text{ tank}}{15 \text{ gallons}}$$ Use dimensional analysis.

$$= \frac{1200 \text{ miles}}{1 \text{ trip}} \cdot \frac{1 \text{ gallon}}{24 \text{ miles}} \cdot \frac{1 \text{ tank}}{15 \text{ gallons}}$$ Divide similar units.

$$= \frac{1200}{360} \cdot \frac{\text{tank}}{\text{trip}}$$ Simplify.

$$= 3\frac{1}{3} \text{ tanks/trip}$$ Simplify.

You can expect to use $3\frac{1}{3}$ tanks of gasoline for the trip.

Exercises

Find each product.

1. $\dfrac{1 \text{ mile}}{8 \text{ blocks}} \cdot \dfrac{32 \text{ blocks}}{3 \text{ hours}}$

2. $\dfrac{8 \text{ centimeters}}{1 \text{ pin}} \cdot \dfrac{1 \text{ meter}}{100 \text{ centimeters}} \cdot \dfrac{1 \text{ kilometer}}{1000 \text{ meters}}$

3. $\dfrac{50 \text{ miles}}{1 \text{ hour}} \cdot \dfrac{5280 \text{ feet}}{1 \text{ mile}} \cdot \dfrac{1 \text{ hour}}{60 \text{ minutes}} \cdot \dfrac{1 \text{ minute}}{60 \text{ seconds}}$

4. $\dfrac{2000 \text{ revolutions}}{1 \text{ minute}} \cdot \dfrac{60 \text{ minutes}}{1 \text{ hour}} \cdot \dfrac{24 \text{ hours}}{1 \text{ day}} \cdot \dfrac{7 \text{ days}}{1 \text{ week}}$

5. **CARPETING** Sarina's living room is 15 feet by 18 feet. What will it cost to carpet the living room if carpet costs $24 per square yard?

6. **CHARITY WALK** Suppose you participate in a walk for charity by asking for pledges. You walk at a constant rate of 2 miles per hour and have pledges totaling $15 per mile. How much do you earn for the charity if you walk for 16 hours?

7. **PAINTING** Suppose you estimate that the exterior of your house will need 15 gallons of paint. You use a special paint sprayer that holds one quart of paint. How many times do you need to fill the sprayer to paint the house?

8. **CALORIES** The number of calories used to play volleyball depends on your weight and how long you play. Playing volleyball expends 2.2 Calories per hour per pound of weight. If you weigh 130 pounds, how many Calories do you use in 1.5 hours?

9. **GARDENING** The rectangular lawns in a tract housing development each measure 100 feet by 200 feet. A gardener can cut 1000 square yards of grass per hour. How many of these lawns can he cut in $6\frac{2}{3}$ hours?

12-4 Study Guide and Intervention

Dividing Rational Expressions

Divide Rational Expressions To divide rational expressions, multiply by the reciprocal of the divisor. Then simplify.

Example 1 Find $\dfrac{12c^2d}{5a^2b^2} \div \dfrac{c^2d^2}{10ab}$.

$$\dfrac{12c^2d}{5a^2b^2} \div \dfrac{c^2d^2}{10ab} = \dfrac{12c^2d}{5a^2b^2} \times \dfrac{10ab}{c^2d^2}$$

$$= \dfrac{12c^2d}{5a^2b^2} \times \dfrac{10ab}{c^2d^2}$$

$$= \dfrac{24}{abd}$$

Example 2 Find $\dfrac{x^2 + 6x - 27}{x^2 + 11x + 18} \div \dfrac{x - 3}{x^2 + x - 2}$.

$$\dfrac{x^2 + 6x - 27}{x^2 + 11x + 18} \div \dfrac{x - 3}{x^2 + x - 2} = \dfrac{x^2 + 6x - 27}{x^2 + 11x + 18} \times \dfrac{x^2 + x - 2}{x - 3}$$

$$= \dfrac{(x + 9)(x - 3)}{(x + 9)(x + 2)} \times \dfrac{(x + 2)(x - 1)}{x - 3}$$

$$= \dfrac{(x + 9)(x - 3)}{(x + 9)(x + 2)} \times \dfrac{(x + 2)(x - 1)}{x - 3}$$

$$= x - 1$$

Exercises

Find each quotient.

1. $\dfrac{12ab}{a^2b^2} \div \dfrac{b}{a}$

2. $\dfrac{n}{4} \div \dfrac{n}{m}$

3. $\dfrac{3xy^2}{8} \div 6xy$

4. $\dfrac{m - 5}{8} \div \dfrac{m - 5}{16}$

5. $\dfrac{2n - 4}{2n} \div \dfrac{n^2 - 4}{n}$

6. $\dfrac{y^2 - 36}{y^2 - 49} \div \dfrac{y + 6}{y + 7}$

7. $\dfrac{x^2 - 5x + 6}{5} \div \dfrac{x - 3}{15}$

8. $\dfrac{a^2b^3c}{3s^2t} \div \dfrac{6a^2bc}{8st^2u}$

9. $\dfrac{x^2 + 6x + 8}{x^2 + 4x + 4} \div \dfrac{x + 4}{x + 2}$

10. $\dfrac{m^2 - 49}{m} \div \dfrac{m^2 - 13m + 42}{3m^2}$

11. $\dfrac{n^2 - 5n + 6}{n^2 + 3n} \div \dfrac{3 - n}{4n + 12}$

12. $\dfrac{p^2 - 2pq + q^2}{p + q} \div \dfrac{p^2 - q^2}{p + q}$

13. $\dfrac{a^2 + 7a + 12}{a^2 + 3a - 10} \div \dfrac{a^2 - 9}{a^2 - 25}$

14. $\dfrac{a^2 - 9}{2a^2 + 13a - 7} \div \dfrac{a + 3}{4a^2 - 1}$

Lesson 12-4

12-4 **Study Guide and Intervention** (continued)

Dividing Rational Expressions

Dimensional Analysis Dividing rational expressions that involve units of measure can also be simplified by dimensional analysis.

Example **SKATING A speed skater skated 1000 meters in 1.14 minutes. Find his speed in meters per minute.**

Use the formula for time and distance, rate · time = distance.

$r \cdot t = d$

$r \cdot 1.14 \text{ minutes} = 1000 \text{ meters}$ $t = 1.14$ minutes, $d = 1000$ meters

$r = 1000 \text{ meters} \div 1.14 \text{ minutes}$ Divide each side by 1.14 minutes.

$= 1000 \text{ m} \cdot \dfrac{1}{1.14 \text{ minutes}}$ Multiply by the reciprocal.

$= \dfrac{1000 \text{ meters}}{1.14 \text{ minutes}}$ Multiply.

$\approx 877.2 \text{ meters/minute}$ Express as a unit rate.

Exercises

Complete.

1. $32 \text{ yd}^3 =$ ___ ft^3

2. $0.48 \text{ m}^3 =$ ___ cm^3

3. $144 \text{ in}^3 =$ ___ ft^3

4. $1400 \text{ m/min} =$ ___ km/min

5. $48 \text{ plants/ft}^2 =$ ___ plants/yd^2

6. $\$9/\text{h} = \$$___$/\text{min}$

7. $40 \text{ m/s} =$ ___ m/min

8. $\$5.04/\text{doz} = \$$___$/\text{piece}$

9. Express 90 kilometers per hour in meters per second.

10. Express 55 miles per hour in miles per minute.

11. Express $4.48 per pound in dollars per ounce.

12. **FOOD PRICES** A 14-ounce box of cereal costs $3.92. If a 16-ounce box of the same cereal costs the same per ounce, how much does the 16-ounce box cost?

13. **BICYCLING** The tires on a bicycle are 30 inches in diameter.

    a. Find the number of revolutions per mile.

    b. How many times per minute do the tires revolve when the bicycle is traveling at 12 miles per hour? Round to the nearest whole number.

14. **COOKING** A certain recipe calls for $\frac{3}{4}$ cup sugar and it makes 36 cookies.

    a. If 8 tablespoons $= \frac{1}{2}$ cup, how many tablespoons of sugar is in each cookie?

    b. Each tablespoon of sugar contains 48 Calories. If each cookie has 160 Calories, what percent of the calories are from sugar?

NAME _____ DATE _____ PERIOD _____

12-5 Study Guide and Intervention

Dividing Polynomials

Divide Polynomials by Monomials To divide a polynomial by a monomial, divide each term of the polynomial by the monomial.

Example 1 Find $(4r^2 - 12r) \div 2r$.

$(4r^2 - 12r) \div 2r = \dfrac{4r^2 - 12r}{2r}$

$= \dfrac{4r^2}{2r} - \dfrac{12r}{2r}$ Divide each term.

$= \dfrac{4r^2}{2r} - \dfrac{12r^{6}}{2r}$ Simplify.

$= 2r - 6$ Simplify.

Example 2 Find $(3x^2 - 8x + 4) \div 4x$.

$(3x^2 - 8x + 4) \div 4x = \dfrac{3x^2 - 8x + 4}{4x}$

$= \dfrac{3x^2}{4x} - \dfrac{8x}{4x} + \dfrac{4}{4x}$

$= \dfrac{3x\,3x^2}{4\,4x} - \dfrac{2\,8x}{1\,4x} + \dfrac{4}{4x}\,x$

$= \dfrac{3x}{4} - 2 + \dfrac{1}{x}$

Exercises

Find each quotient.

1. $(x^3 + 2x^2 - x) \div x$

2. $(2x^3 + 12x^2 - 8x) \div 2x$

3. $(x^2 + 3x - 4) \div x$

4. $(4m^2 + 6m - 8) \div 2m^2$

5. $(3x^3 + 15x^2 - 21x) \div 3x$

6. $(8m^2n^2 + 4mn - 8n) \div n$

7. $(8y^4 + 16y^2 - 4) \div 4y^2$

8. $(16x^4y^2 + 24xy + 5) \div xy$

9. $\dfrac{15x^2 - 25x + 30}{5}$

10. $\dfrac{10a^2b + 12ab - 8b}{2a}$

11. $\dfrac{6x^3 + 9x^2 + 9}{3x}$

12. $\dfrac{m^2 - 12m + 42}{3m^2}$

13. $\dfrac{m^2n^2 - 5mn + 6}{m^2n^2}$

14. $\dfrac{p^2 - 4pq + 6q^2}{pq}$

15. $\dfrac{6a^2b^2 - 8ab + 12}{2a^2}$

16. $\dfrac{2x^2y^3 - 4x^2y^2 - 8xy}{2xy}$

17. $\dfrac{9x^2y^2z - 2xyz + 12x}{xy}$

18. $\dfrac{2a^3b^3 + 8a^2b^2 - 10ab + 12}{2a^2b^2}$

© Glencoe/McGraw-Hill   **167**   *Glencoe Algebra 1*

Lesson 12-5

12-5 Study Guide and Intervention *(continued)*

Dividing Polynomials

Divide Polynomials by Binomials To divide a polynomial by a binomial, factor the dividend if possible and divide both dividend and divisor by the GCF. If the polynomial cannot be factored, use long division.

Example Find $(x^2 + 7x + 10) \div (x + 3)$.

Step 1 Divide the first term of the dividend, x^2 by the first term of the divisor, x.

$$\begin{array}{r} x \\ x + 3 \overline{)x^2 + 7x + 10} \\ \underline{(-)\, x^2 + 3x} \\ 4x \end{array}$$

Multiply x and $x + 3$.

Subtract.

Step 2 Bring down the next term, 10. Divide the first term of $4x + 10$ by x.

$$\begin{array}{r} x + 4 \\ x + 3 \overline{)x^2 + 7x + 10} \\ \underline{x^2 + 3x} \\ 4x + 10 \\ \underline{(-)\, 4x + 12} \\ -2 \end{array}$$

Multiply 4 and $x + 3$.

Subtract.

The quotient is $x + 4$ with remainder -2. The quotient can be written as $x + 4 + \dfrac{-2}{x + 3}$.

Exercises

Find each quotient.

1. $(b^2 - 5b + 6) \div (b - 2)$

2. $(x^2 - x - 6) \div (x - 3)$

3. $(x^2 + 3x - 4) \div (x - 1)$

4. $(m^2 + 2m - 8) \div (m + 4)$

5. $(x^2 + 5x + 6) \div (x + 2)$

6. $(m^2 + 4m + 4) \div (m + 2)$

7. $(2y^2 + 5y + 2) \div (y + 2)$

8. $(8y^2 - 15y - 2) \div (y - 2)$

9. $\dfrac{8x^2 - 6x - 9}{4x + 3}$

10. $\dfrac{m^2 - 5m - 6}{m - 6}$

11. $\dfrac{x^3 + 1}{x - 2}$

12. $\dfrac{6m^3 + 11m^2 + 4m + 35}{2m + 5}$

13. $\dfrac{6a^2 + 7a + 5}{2a + 5}$

14. $\dfrac{8p^3 + 27}{2p + 3}$

12-6 Study Guide and Intervention

Rational Expressions With Like Denominators

Add Rational Expressions To add rational expressions with like denominators, add the numerators and then write the sum over the common denominator. If possible, simplify the resulting rational expression.

Example 1 Find $\dfrac{5n}{15} + \dfrac{7n}{15}$.

$\dfrac{5n}{15} + \dfrac{7n}{15} = \dfrac{5n + 7n}{15}$ Add the numerators.

$= \dfrac{12n}{15}$ Simplify.

$= \dfrac{12n}{15}\,^{4n}_{\;5}$ Divide by 3.

$= \dfrac{4n}{5}$ Simplify.

Example 2 Find $\dfrac{3x}{x + 2} + \dfrac{6}{x + 2}$.

$\dfrac{3x}{x + 2} + \dfrac{6}{x + 2} = \dfrac{3x + 6}{x + 2}$

$= \dfrac{3(x + 2)}{x + 2}$

$= \dfrac{3(x + 2)^{\,1}}{x + 2^{\,1}}$

$= \dfrac{3}{1}$ or 3

Exercises

Find each sum.

1. $\dfrac{3}{a} + \dfrac{4}{a}$

2. $\dfrac{x^2}{8} + \dfrac{x}{8}$

3. $\dfrac{x + 3}{6} + \dfrac{x - 2}{6}$

4. $\dfrac{m - 8}{2} + \dfrac{m + 4}{2}$

5. $\dfrac{2x}{x + 5} + \dfrac{3x}{x + 5}$

6. $\dfrac{m + 4}{m - 1} + \dfrac{m + 4}{m - 1}$

7. $\dfrac{y + 5}{y + 6} + \dfrac{1}{y + 6}$

8. $\dfrac{3x + 5}{5} + \dfrac{2x + 10}{5}$

9. $\dfrac{2a - 4}{a - 4} + \dfrac{-a}{a - 4}$

10. $\dfrac{m + 1}{2m - 1} + \dfrac{3m - 3}{2m - 1}$

11. $\dfrac{x + 1}{x - 2} + \dfrac{x - 5}{x - 2}$

12. $\dfrac{5a}{3b^2} + \dfrac{10a}{3b^2}$

13. $\dfrac{3x + 2}{x + 2} + \dfrac{x + 6}{x + 2}$

14. $\dfrac{a - 4}{a + 1} + \dfrac{a + 6}{a + 1}$

15. $\dfrac{2x + 3}{x + 3} + \dfrac{x + 6}{x + 3}$

16. $\dfrac{3a^2 + 4a}{a} + \dfrac{6a^2}{a}$

17. $\dfrac{-8x}{x - 4} + \dfrac{4x + x^2}{x - 4}$

18. $\dfrac{9a - 14}{2a + 1} + \dfrac{8a + 16}{2a + 1}$

12-6 **Study Guide and Intervention** (continued)

Rational Expressions with Like Denominators

Subtract Rational Expressions To subtract fractions with like denominators, subtract the numerators and then write the difference over the common denominator. If possible, simplify the resulting rational expression.

Example Find $\dfrac{3x + 2}{x - 2} - \dfrac{4x}{x - 2}$.

$$\dfrac{3x + 2}{x - 2} - \dfrac{4x}{x - 2} = \dfrac{3x + 2 - 4x}{x - 2}$$ The common denominator is $x - 2$.

$$= \dfrac{2 - x}{x - 2}$$ Subtract.

$$= \dfrac{-1(x - 2)}{x - 2}$$ $2 - x = -1(x - 2)$

$$= \dfrac{-1(x - 2)^1}{x - 2^1}$$

$$= \dfrac{-1}{1}$$ Simplify.

$$= -1$$

Exercises

Find each difference.

1. $\dfrac{3}{a} - \dfrac{5}{a}$

2. $\dfrac{5x}{8} - \dfrac{x}{8}$

3. $\dfrac{5x}{9} - \dfrac{x}{9}$

4. $\dfrac{11x}{15y} - \dfrac{x}{15y}$

5. $\dfrac{8t}{w + 6} - \dfrac{3t}{w + 6}$

6. $\dfrac{7m + 1}{3m + 1} - \dfrac{4m}{3m + 1}$

7. $\dfrac{y + 7}{y + 6} - \dfrac{1}{y + 6}$

8. $\dfrac{3y + 5}{5} - \dfrac{2y}{5}$

9. $\dfrac{2a + 8}{a + 4} - \dfrac{a + 4}{a + 4}$

10. $\dfrac{m + 1}{2m - 3} - \dfrac{3m - 2}{2m - 3}$

11. $\dfrac{x^2 + x}{x} - \dfrac{x^2 + 5x}{x}$

12. $\dfrac{5a + 2}{a^2} - \dfrac{4a + 2}{a^2}$

13. $\dfrac{c^2}{c + 2} - \dfrac{4}{c + 2}$

14. $\dfrac{a - 4}{a + 1} - \dfrac{a + 6}{a + 1}$

15. $\dfrac{x^2 + 2x}{x - 4} - \dfrac{x^2 + 8}{x - 4}$

16. $\dfrac{a}{a^2 - 1} - \dfrac{1}{a^2 - 1}$

17. $\dfrac{4x - 4y}{4x + 4y} - \dfrac{4x}{4x + 4y}$

18. $\dfrac{x^2 + x}{x - 2} - \dfrac{6}{x - 2}$

12-7 Study Guide and Intervention

Rational Expressions with Unlike Denominators

Add Rational Expressions Adding rational expressions with unlike denominators is similar to adding fractions with unlike denominators.

Adding Rational Expressions	**Step 1** Find the LCD of the expressions.
	Step 2 Change each expression into an equivalent expression with the LCD as the denominator.
	Step 3 Add just as with expressions with like denominators.
	Step 4 Simplify if necessary.

Example 1 Find $\dfrac{n+3}{n} + \dfrac{8n-4}{4n}$.

Factor each denominator.

$n = n$

$4n = 4 \cdot n$

LCD $= 4n$

Since the denominator of $\dfrac{8n-4}{4n}$ is already

$4n$, only $\dfrac{n+3}{n}$ needs to be renamed.

$\dfrac{n+3}{n} + \dfrac{8n-4}{4n} = \dfrac{4(n+3)}{4n} + \dfrac{8n-4}{4n}$

$= \dfrac{4n+12}{4n} + \dfrac{8n-4}{4n}$

$= \dfrac{12n+8}{4n}$

$= \dfrac{3n+2}{n}$

Example 2 Find $\dfrac{1}{2x^2+6x} + \dfrac{3}{x^2}$.

$\dfrac{1}{2x^2+6x} + \dfrac{3}{x^2} = \dfrac{1}{2x(x+3)} + \dfrac{3}{x^2}$

$= \dfrac{1}{2x(x+3)} \cdot \dfrac{x}{x} + \dfrac{3}{x^2} \cdot \dfrac{2(x+3)}{2(x+3)}$

$= \dfrac{x}{2x^2(x+3)} + \dfrac{6(x+3)}{2x^2(x+3)}$

$= \dfrac{x+6x+18}{2x^2(x+3)}$

$= \dfrac{7x+18}{2x^2(x+3)}$

Exercises

Find each sum.

1. $\dfrac{1}{a} + \dfrac{7}{3a}$

2. $\dfrac{1}{6x} + \dfrac{3}{8}$

3. $\dfrac{4}{9x} + \dfrac{5}{x^2}$

4. $\dfrac{2}{x^2} + \dfrac{3}{x^3}$

5. $\dfrac{8}{4a^2} + \dfrac{6}{3a}$

6. $\dfrac{4}{h+1} + \dfrac{2}{h+2}$

7. $\dfrac{4}{y+6} + \dfrac{1}{y+2}$

8. $\dfrac{y}{y^2+4y+4} + \dfrac{2}{y+2}$

9. $\dfrac{a}{a+4} + \dfrac{4}{a-4}$

10. $\dfrac{6}{3(m+1)} + \dfrac{2}{3(m-1)}$

11. $\dfrac{4x}{6x-2y} + \dfrac{3y}{9x-3y}$

12. $\dfrac{a-2}{a^2-4} + \dfrac{a-2}{a+2}$

13. $\dfrac{y+2}{y^2+5y+6} + \dfrac{2-y}{y^2+y-6}$

14. $\dfrac{q}{q^2-16} + \dfrac{q+1}{q^2+5q+4}$

12-7 **Study Guide and Intervention** *(continued)*

Rational Expressions with Unlike Denominators

Subtract Rational Expressions Adapt the steps given on page 741 for adding rational expressions. In Step 3, subtract the numerators instead of adding them.

Example **Find** $\dfrac{3x}{x^2 - 4x} - \dfrac{1}{x - 4}$.

$$\dfrac{3x}{x^2 - 4x} - \dfrac{1}{x - 4} = \dfrac{3x}{x(x - 4)} - \dfrac{1}{x - 4} \qquad \text{Factor the denominator.}$$

$$= \dfrac{3x}{x(x - 4)} - \dfrac{1}{x - 4} \cdot \dfrac{x}{x} \qquad \text{The LCD is } x(x - 4).$$

$$= \dfrac{3x}{x(x - 4)} - \dfrac{x}{x(x - 4)} \qquad 1 \cdot x = x$$

$$= \dfrac{2x}{x(x - 4)} \qquad \text{Subtract numerators.}$$

$$= \dfrac{2}{x - 4} \qquad \text{Simplify.}$$

Exercises

Find each difference.

1. $\dfrac{1}{a} - \dfrac{9}{4a}$

2. $\dfrac{1}{9x} - \dfrac{1}{8}$

3. $\dfrac{5}{9x} - \dfrac{1}{x^2}$

4. $\dfrac{6}{x^2} - \dfrac{3}{x^3}$

5. $\dfrac{5}{4a^2} - \dfrac{2}{3a}$

6. $\dfrac{h}{6h + 6} - \dfrac{1}{h + 1}$

7. $\dfrac{y}{y - 3} - \dfrac{3}{y + 3}$

8. $\dfrac{y}{y - 7} - \dfrac{y + 3}{y^2 - 4y - 21}$

9. $\dfrac{7a + 4}{3a + 9} - \dfrac{2a}{a + 3}$

10. $\dfrac{5}{m + 1} - \dfrac{2}{3(m - 1)}$

11. $\dfrac{4}{x - 2y} - \dfrac{2}{x + 2y}$

12. $\dfrac{a - 6b}{2a^2 - 5ab + 2b^2} - \dfrac{7}{a - 2b}$

13. $\dfrac{2}{y^2 + 3y + 2} - \dfrac{4}{y^2 + 2y + 1}$

14. $\dfrac{q}{q^2 + 2q + 1} - \dfrac{1}{q^2 + 5q + 4}$

12-8 Study Guide and Intervention

Mixed Expressions and Complex Fractions

Simplify Mixed Expressions Algebraic expressions such as $a + \dfrac{b}{c}$ and $5 + \dfrac{x+y}{x+3}$ are called **mixed expressions**. Changing mixed expressions to rational expressions is similar to changing mixed numbers to improper fractions.

Example 1 Simplify $5 + \dfrac{2}{n}$.

$5 + \dfrac{2}{n} = \dfrac{5 \cdot n}{n} + \dfrac{2}{n}$ LCD is n.

$\quad = \dfrac{5n + 2}{n}$ Add the numerators.

Therefore, $5 + \dfrac{2}{n} = \dfrac{5n + 2}{n}$.

Example 2 Simplify $2 + \dfrac{3}{n+3}$.

$2 + \dfrac{3}{n+3} = \dfrac{2(n+3)}{n+3} + \dfrac{3}{n+3}$

$\quad = \dfrac{2n+6}{n+3} + \dfrac{3}{n+3}$

$\quad = \dfrac{2n+6+3}{n+3}$

$\quad = \dfrac{2n+9}{n+3}$

Therefore, $2 + \dfrac{3}{n+3} = \dfrac{2n+9}{n+3}$.

Exercises

Write each mixed expression as a rational expression.

1. $4 + \dfrac{6}{a}$

2. $\dfrac{1}{9x} - 3$

3. $3x - \dfrac{1}{x^2}$

4. $\dfrac{4}{x^2} - 2$

5. $10 + \dfrac{60}{x+5}$

6. $\dfrac{h}{h+4} + 2$

7. $\dfrac{y}{y-2} + y^2$

8. $4 - \dfrac{4}{2x+1}$

9. $1 + \dfrac{1}{x}$

10. $\dfrac{4}{m-2} - 2m$

11. $x^2 + \dfrac{x+2}{x-3}$

12. $a - 3 + \dfrac{a-2}{a+3}$

13. $4m + \dfrac{3n}{2t}$

14. $2q^2 + \dfrac{q}{p+q}$

15. $\dfrac{2}{y^2-1} - 4y^2$

16. $q^2 + \dfrac{p+q}{p-q}$

Lesson 12-8

12-8 Study Guide and Intervention *(continued)*

Mixed Expressions and Complex Fractions

Simplify Complex Fractions If a fraction has one or more fractions in the numerator or denominator, it is called a **complex fraction**.

Simplifying a Complex Fraction	Any complex fraction $\dfrac{\frac{a}{b}}{\frac{c}{d}}$ where $b \neq 0$, $c \neq 0$, and $d \neq 0$, can be expressed as $\dfrac{ad}{bc}$.

Example Simplify $\dfrac{2+\frac{4}{a}}{\frac{a+2}{3}}$.

$\dfrac{2+\frac{4}{a}}{\frac{a+2}{3}} = \dfrac{\frac{2a}{a}+\frac{4}{a}}{\frac{a+2}{3}}$ Find the LCD for the numerator and rewrite as like fractions.

$= \dfrac{\frac{2a+4}{a}}{\frac{a+2}{3}}$ Simplify the numerator.

$= \dfrac{2a+4}{a} \cdot \dfrac{3}{a+2}$ Rewrite as the product of the numerator and the reciprocal of the denominator.

$= \dfrac{2(a+2)}{a} \cdot \dfrac{3}{a+2}$ Factor.

$= \dfrac{6}{a}$ Divide and simplify.

Exercises

Simplify each expression.

1. $\dfrac{2\frac{2}{5}}{3\frac{3}{4}}$

2. $\dfrac{\frac{3}{x}}{\frac{4}{y}}$

3. $\dfrac{\frac{x}{y^3}}{\frac{x^3}{y^2}}$

4. $\dfrac{1-\frac{1}{x}}{1+\frac{1}{x}}$

5. $\dfrac{1-\frac{1}{x}}{1-\frac{1}{x^2}}$

6. $\dfrac{\frac{1}{x-3}}{\frac{2}{x^2-9}}$

7. $\dfrac{\frac{x^2-25}{y}}{x^3-5x^2}$

8. $\dfrac{x-\frac{12}{x-1}}{x-\frac{8}{x-2}}$

9. $\dfrac{\frac{3}{y+2}-\frac{2}{y-2}}{\frac{1}{y+2}-\frac{2}{y-2}}$

12-9 Study Guide and Intervention

Solving Rational Equations

Solve Rational Equations **Rational equations** are equations that contain rational expressions. To solve equations containing rational expressions, multiply each side of the equation by the least common denominator.

Rational equations can be used to solve **work problems** and **rate problems**.

Example 1 Solve $\dfrac{x-3}{3} + \dfrac{x}{2} = 4$.

$\dfrac{x-3}{3} + \dfrac{x}{2} = 4$

$6\left(\dfrac{x-3}{3} + \dfrac{x}{2}\right) = 6(4)$ The LCD is 6.

$2(x-3) + 3x = 24$ Distributive Property

$2x - 6 + 3x = 24$ Distributive Property

$5x = 30$ Simplify.

$x = 6$ Divide each side by 5.

The solution is 6.

Example 2 **WORK PROBLEM Marla can paint Percy's kitchen in 3 hours. Percy can paint it in 2 hours. Working together, how long will it take Marla and Percy to paint the kitchen?**

In t hours, Marla completes $t \cdot \dfrac{1}{3}$ of the job and Percy completes $t \cdot \dfrac{1}{2}$ of the job. So an equation for completing the whole job is $\dfrac{t}{3} + \dfrac{t}{2} = 1$.

$\dfrac{t}{3} + \dfrac{t}{2} = 1$

$2t + 3t = 6$ Multiply each term by 6.

$5t = 6$ Add like terms.

$t = \dfrac{6}{5}$ Solve.

So it will take Marla and Percy $1\dfrac{1}{5}$ hours to paint the room if they work together.

Exercises

Solve each equation.

1. $\dfrac{x-5}{5} + \dfrac{x}{4} = 8$

2. $\dfrac{3}{x} = \dfrac{6}{x+1}$

3. $\dfrac{x-1}{5} = \dfrac{2x-2}{15}$

4. $\dfrac{8}{n-1} = \dfrac{10}{n+1}$

5. $s - \dfrac{4}{s+3} = s + 3$

6. $\dfrac{m+4}{m} + \dfrac{m}{3} = \dfrac{m}{3}$

7. $\dfrac{q+4}{q-1} + \dfrac{q}{q+1} = 2$

8. $\dfrac{5-2x}{2} - \dfrac{4x+3}{6} = \dfrac{7x+2}{6}$

9. $\dfrac{m+1}{m-1} - \dfrac{m}{1-m} = 1$

10. $\dfrac{x^2-9}{x-3} + x^2 = 9$

11. **GREETING CARDS** It takes Kenesha 45 minutes to prepare 20 greeting cards. It takes Paula 30 minutes to prepare the same number of cards. Working together at this rate, how long will it take them to prepare the cards?

12. **BOATING** A motorboat went upstream at 15 miles per hour and returned downstream at 20 miles per hour. How far did the boat travel one way if the round trip took 3.5 hours?

Lesson 12-9

12-9 Study Guide and Intervention *(continued)*

Solving Rational Equations

Extraneous Solutions When you use cross multiplication or use the LCD of two rational expressions, you may get values for the variable that are not solutions of the original equation. Such values are called **extraneous solutions**.

Example Solve $\dfrac{15}{x^2 - 1} = \dfrac{5}{2(x - 1)}$.

$\dfrac{15}{x^2 - 1} = \dfrac{5}{2(x - 1)}$ Original equation

$30(x - 1) = 5(x^2 - 1)$ Cross multiply.

$30x - 30 = 5x^2 - 5$ Distributive Property

$0 = 5x^2 - 30x + 30 - 5$ Add $-30x + 30$ to each side.

$0 = 5x^2 - 30x + 25$ Simplify.

$0 = 5(x^2 - 6x + 5)$ Factor.

$0 = 5(x - 1)(x - 5)$ Factor.

$x = 1$ or $x = 5$ Zero Product Property

The number 1 is an extraneous solution, since 1 is an excluded value for x. So, 5 is the solution of the equation.

Exercises

Solve each equation. State any extraneous solutions.

1. $\dfrac{6x}{x - 1} + \dfrac{2x - 8}{x - 1} = 4$

2. $\dfrac{4x}{-x - 2} = \dfrac{1}{x + 2}$

3. $\dfrac{-5}{x + 2} = \dfrac{x - 1}{3}$

4. $\dfrac{x}{x - 3} + \dfrac{4}{3 - x} = x$

5. $\dfrac{x}{x - 2} - \dfrac{4}{2 - x} = x$

6. $\dfrac{x}{x^2 - 25} = \dfrac{1}{x - 5}$

7. $\dfrac{x}{x^2 - 36} - \dfrac{1}{x - 6} = 0$

8. $\dfrac{4z}{z^2 + 4z + 3} = \dfrac{6}{z + 3} + \dfrac{4}{z + 1}$

9. $\dfrac{4}{4 - p} - \dfrac{p^2}{p - 4} = 4$

10. $\dfrac{x^2 - 16}{x - 4} + x^2 = 16$

13-1 Study Guide and Intervention

Sampling and Bias

Sampling Techniques Suppose you want to survey students about their choice of radio stations. All students make up the **population** you want to survey. A **sample** is some portion of the larger group that you select to represent the entire group. A **census** would include all students within the population. A **random sample** of a population is selected so that it is representative of the entire population.

Simple Random Sample	a sample that is as likely to be chosen as another from a population
Stratified Random Sample	A population is first divided into similar, nonoverlapping groups. A simple random sample is then chosen from each group.
Systematic Random Sample	Items are selected according to a specified time or interval.

Example 1 SCHOOL Ten students are chosen randomly from each high school class to be on an advisory committee with the principal.

a. **Identify the sample and suggest a population from which it was chosen.**

The sample is 4 groups of 10 students each from the freshmen, sophomore, junior, and senior classes. The population is the entire student body of the school.

b. **Classify the sample as *simple*, *stratified*, or *systematic*.**

This is a stratified random sample because the population was first divided into nonoverlapping groups and then a random sample was chosen from each group.

Example 2 DOOR PRIZES Each of the participants in a conference was given a numbered name tag. Twenty-five numbers were chosen at random to receive a door prize.

a. **Identify the sample and suggest a population from which it was chosen.**

The sample was 25 participants of the conference. The population was all of the participants of the conference.

b. **Classify the sample as *simple*, *stratified*, or *systematic*.**

Since the numbers were chosen randomly, this is a simple random sample because each participant was equally likely to be chosen.

Exercises

Identify each sample, suggest a population from which it was selected, and classify the sample as *simple*, *stratified*, or *systematic*.

1. **SCHOOL** Each student in a class of 25 students was given a number at the beginning of the year. Periodically, the teacher chooses 4 numbers at random to display their homework on the overhead projector.

2. **GARDENING** A gardener divided a lot into 25-square-foot sections. He then took 2 soil samples from each and tested the samples for mineral content.

3. **SCHOOL** One hundred students in the lunch room are chosen for a survey. All students in the school eat lunch at the same time.

4. **SHOPPING** Every tenth person leaving a grocery store was asked if they would participate in a community survey.

13-1 Study Guide and Intervention (continued)

Sampling and Bias

Biased Sample A **biased sample** is one in which one or more parts of the population is favored over the other. Random samples are unbiased because each unit is selected without favoritism.

Biased samples include **convenience samples** in which members of the population are included because they are the most convenient to choose. A **voluntary response sample** is another type of biased sample that includes only those members of the population who choose to participate in the sampling.

Example SCHOOL **The principal of a high school wanted to know if students in the school liked the attendance policy. He decided to survey the students in the third-hour study hall about whether they like the attendance policy. Fewer than one fourth of the students in the school have a study hall.**

a. **Identify the sample and suggest a population from which it is chosen.**

The sample includes only those students in the third-hour study hall. The population is the entire student body.

b. **Classify the sample as** *convenience* **or** *voluntary response*.

This sample is a convenience sample because it is convenient to sample students in a study hall during a certain period of the day.

Exercises

Identify each sample, suggest a population from which it was selected, and classify the sample as *convenience* or *voluntary response*.

1. **SCHOOL** The high school administration wanted to evaluate how homecoming week was conducted at the school. Each female member of the Student Council at the high school was asked if she liked homecoming activities.

2. **MANUFACTURING** A clothing company wanted to check quality control of all its products. The plant manager decided to look at every fourth item inspected by Inspector X. There are 10 inspectors in the plant.

3. **SCHOOL** The counselors of a high school sent out a survey to senior students with questions about their plans for college. Some students did not plan to attend college. 40% of the seniors sent responses back.

4. **BUSINESS** A marketing group was asked to compile data on the effectiveness of advertisements for household products across the country. The group chose to conduct surveys at shopping malls. Every person walking by a survey taker in a shopping mall was asked if he/she would participate in a survey about household products.

13-2 Study Guide and Intervention

Introduction to Matrices

Organize Data in Matrices A **matrix** is a rectangular arrangement of numbers in rows and columns. It is described by its **dimensions**, the number of rows and columns in the matrix, with the number of rows as the first number. Each number in the matrix is called an **element**.

Example State the dimensions of each matrix. Then identify the position of the circled element in each matrix.

a. $[4 \quad -7 \quad ⑭ \quad 2]$

The matrix has one row and four columns. Therefore, it is a 1-by-4 matrix. The circled element is in the first row and the third column.

b. $\begin{bmatrix} -2 & 3 \\ 4 & -1 \\ 5 & ① \end{bmatrix}$

The matrix has three rows and two columns. Therefore, it is a 3-by-2 matrix. The circled element is in the third row and the second column.

Exercises

State the dimensions of each matrix. Then identify the position of the circled element in each matrix.

1. $\begin{bmatrix} 1 \\ 5 \\ -2 \\ ④ \end{bmatrix}$

2. $\begin{bmatrix} 3 & -2 & -3 \\ 4 & ⑤ & -4 \\ 5 & 1 & 7 \end{bmatrix}$

3. $[⑦ \quad 9 \quad -2]$

4. $\begin{bmatrix} 3 & -3 \\ -1 & -4 \\ 5 & ⊖6 \\ 7 & 0 \end{bmatrix}$

5. $\begin{bmatrix} 2 & -4 \\ 5 & ⊖1 \end{bmatrix}$

6. $[⊖1 \quad 2]$

7. $\begin{bmatrix} 1 & -2 \\ 5 & ⑤ \\ 3 & 7 \\ -3 & 4 \end{bmatrix}$

8. $\begin{bmatrix} -3 & ② & -3 \\ 4 & -5 & 4 \end{bmatrix}$

9. $[7 \quad 6 \quad -2 \quad ⊖1]$

10. $\begin{bmatrix} 3 & 5 & -3 \\ -1 & 4 & -2 \\ 5 & 6 & ⊖1 \end{bmatrix}$

11. $\begin{bmatrix} -2 & -4 \\ ⑨ & 1 \end{bmatrix}$

12. $[⑧]$

© Glencoe/McGraw-Hill

Glencoe Algebra 1

Lesson 13-2

13-2 Study Guide and Intervention (continued)

Introduction to Matrices

Matrix Operations Matrices can be added or subtracted if they have the same dimensions. To do this, you add or subtract corresponding elements of the two matrices. A matrix can also be multiplied by a constant number called a **scalar**. To do this, multiply each element of the matrix by the scalar.

Example Given $A = \begin{bmatrix} 3 & -3 \\ -2 & 4 \\ -5 & 2 \end{bmatrix}$, $B = \begin{bmatrix} -3 & -4 \\ 0 & 5 \\ -5 & 1 \end{bmatrix}$, and $C = \begin{bmatrix} -2 & 3 \\ 1 & 4 \end{bmatrix}$, find each of the following.

a. $A + B$

$$A + B = \begin{bmatrix} 3 & -3 \\ -2 & 4 \\ -5 & 2 \end{bmatrix} + \begin{bmatrix} -3 & -4 \\ 0 & 5 \\ -5 & 1 \end{bmatrix} = \begin{bmatrix} 3 + (-3) & -3 + (-4) \\ -2 + 0 & 4 + 5 \\ -5 + (-5) & 2 + 1 \end{bmatrix} = \begin{bmatrix} 0 & -7 \\ -2 & 9 \\ -10 & 3 \end{bmatrix}$$

b. $3C$

$$3C = 3\begin{bmatrix} -2 & 3 \\ 1 & 4 \end{bmatrix} = \begin{bmatrix} 3(-2) & 3(3) \\ 3(1) & 3(4) \end{bmatrix} = \begin{bmatrix} -6 & 9 \\ 3 & 12 \end{bmatrix}$$

Exercises

If $A = \begin{bmatrix} 1 & 3 & -4 \\ -2 & -1 & 4 \\ 7 & 2 & -3 \end{bmatrix}$, $B = \begin{bmatrix} -4 & 3 & -2 \\ 5 & 4 & -1 \\ -4 & 2 & 8 \end{bmatrix}$, $C = \begin{bmatrix} 3 & -3 & 1 \\ -4 & 6 & 2 \end{bmatrix}$, and $D = \begin{bmatrix} 3 & -1 & 9 \\ -6 & 4 & 5 \end{bmatrix}$, find each sum, difference, or product. If the sum or difference does not exist, write *impossible*.

1. $A + B$

2. $C - D$

3. $2A - B$

4. $4D$

5. $B - A$

6. $4D + 2C$

7. $2D + A$

8. $3B - 2A$

9. $-2C$

13-3 Study Guide and Intervention

Histograms

Interpret Data in Histograms A **histogram** is a bar graph in which the data are organized into equal intervals. In a histogram, the horizontal axis shows the range of data values separated into **measurement classes**, and the vertical axis shows the number of values, or **frequency**, in each class.

Example

SCHOOL Answer each question about the histogram shown.

a. In what measurement class does the median occur?

First add the frequencies to determine the number of state scores:
$1 + 1 + 6 + 12 + 24 + 7 = 51$. There are 51 scores. Therefore, the middle data value is the 26th value. The median value is in the 21.1–22.1 measurement class.

*Includes Washington, DC

Source: www.act.org

b. Describe the distribution of the data.

- Only two states have a composite score less than 19.1.
- Almost half of the states have a composite score in the 21.1–22.1 range.
- More than half of the states have a composite score above 21.1.
- The distribution is skewed to the right.

Exercises

For each histogram, answer the following.
- **In what measurement class does the median occur?**
- **Describe the distribution of the data.**

1.
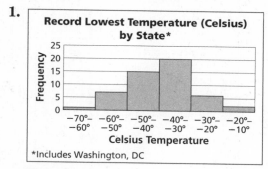

*Includes Washington, DC

Source: *Almanac 2001*

2.
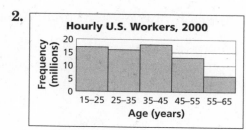

Source: *The World Almanac*

Lesson 13-3

13-3 **Study Guide and Intervention** (continued)

Histograms

Display Data in a Histogram Data from a list or from a **frequency table** can be used to create a histogram.

Example Create a histogram to represent the following scores for a 100-point math test.

72, 84, 85, 91, 98, 90, 68, 65, 55, 71, 91, 99, 98, 59, 60, 64, 61, 68, 88, 91, 99

a. Identify the greatest and least values in the data set.

The test scores range from 55 to 99.

b. Create measurement classes of equal width.

For these data, use measurement classes from 50 to 100 with a 10-point interval for each one.

c. Create a frequency table using the measurement classes.

Score Intervals	Tally	Frequency
$50 \le s < 60$	II	2
$60 \le s < 70$	⊪I	6
$70 \le s < 80$	II	2
$80 \le s < 90$	III	3
$90 \le s < 100$	⊪III	8

d. Draw the histogram.

Exercises

Create a histogram to represent each data set.

1. Student grades on a quiz worth 30 points:

   18, 19, 25, 20, 24, 23, 18, 16, 24, 25, 25, 20,
   20, 20, 17, 19, 20, 23, 25, 21, 27, 29, 29, 28

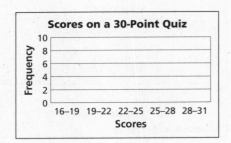

2. Number of red jelly beans found in a bag of jelly beans:

   50, 48, 92, 71, 75, 67, 78, 75, 45, 89, 92,
   65, 45, 67, 78, 67, 88, 59, 70, 75, 74, 72

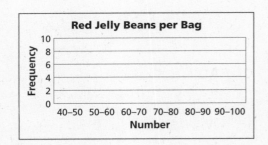

13-4 Study Guide and Intervention

Measures of Variation

Range A **measure of variation** called the **range** describes the spread of numbers in a set of data. The range of a set of data is the difference between the highest and the lowest value.

Example 1 The number of wins for the baseball teams of the American League Central Division are shown at the right. Find the range of the number of wins.

The greatest number of wins is 95 and the least number of wins is 69: $95 - 69 = 26$.

The range is 26.

Major League Final Standings, 2000	
Team	**Wins**
Chicago White Sox	95
Cleveland Indians	90
Detroit Tigers	79
Kansas City Royals	77
Minnesota Twins	69

Source: cbs.sportsline.com

Example 2 Find the range of the student grades below.
58, 95, 72, 85, 84, 88, 91, 92, 93, 45, 80, 81, 92, 93, 50, 79, 84

Since the highest score is 95 and the lowest score is 45, the range is $95 - 45$ or 50.

Exercises

Find the range of each set of data.

1.

Month	Days Below 32°F
November	5
December	20
January	21
February	15
March	8

2.

3. 4, 5, 5, 4, 4, 6, 5, 5

4. 1, 7, 12, 10

5. 3, 0, 4, 9, 6, 4, 0, 1

6. 1.5, 0.5, 2, 3, 2.5

7.

Stem	Leaf
1	2 3 4 6 7 8
2	1 5 5 6 7 8 9
3	0 0 2 3 $1|2 = 12$

8.

Stem	Leaf
18	3 4 6 7
19	0 0 4
20	1 2 2 3 8 8
21	3 4 7 $18|3 = 183$

9. RACING In five pre-race trials, a stock car driver recorded the following speeds in miles per hour: 155, 158, 163, 187, 172. Find the range.

10. SWIMMING The swimming times in seconds for the 50-yard butterfly were 36.30, 35.00, 31.60, 34.00, 35.52, 36.39, 38.87, and 41.62. Find the range.

Lesson 13-4

13-4 Study Guide and Intervention (continued)

Measures of Variation

Quartiles and Interquartile Range Three **quartiles** divide data into four equal parts. The **upper quartile** divides the top half into two equal parts. The **lower quartile** divides the bottom half into two equal parts. The **middle quartile** is the median of the data. The upper and lower quartile values are used to determine the **interquartile range**, another measure of variation

Example Find the lower quartile, the upper quartile, and the interquartile range for the data set 23, 23, 31, 31, 63, 63, 69, 71, 72, 82, 88, 160.

Step 1 Find the median.
   The data are already in order. Since there are an even number of values, the median is the average of the middle two values, 63 and 69. The median is 66.

Step 2 Find the median of the lower half.
   There are two middle values of the lower half of the data, both of which are 31. So 31 is the lower quartile.

Step 3 Find the median of the upper half.
   The middle value of the upper half of the data is the average of the middle two values, 72 and 82. This average is 77. So 77 is the upper quartile.

Step 4 The interquartile range is 77 − 31 or 46.

Exercises

Find the median, lower quartile, upper quartile, and interquartile range of each set of data.

1.

Tallest Trees of the U.S.	
Type of Tree	**Height in Feet**
Giant Sequoia	275
Giant Redwood	321
Sitka Spruce	191
Coast Douglas Fir	281
Sugar Pine	232
Port Orford Cedar	219

Source: The World Almanac

2.

3. 4, 5, 5, 4, 4, 6, 5, 7, 9, 9

4. 1, 7, 12, 10, 21, 32, 24, 19

5. 3, 0, 4, 8, 5, 4, 0, 1, 7, 9, 2, 4, 8

6. 80, 90, 94, 95, 100, 102, 83, 94, 78

7.

Stem	Leaf
1	0 3 5 6 7 8 8
2	1 4 5 6 7 7 8
3	0 0 1 2 3
4	6 8 9 1|0 = 10

8.

Stem	Leaf
20	3 4 6 7 9 9
21	0 0 6 8
22	1 2 2 5 7 8
23	3 4 7 8 20|3 = 203

13-5 Study Guide and Intervention

Box-and-Whisker Plots

Box-and-Whisker Plots A **box-and-whisker plot** displays the extremes, the quartiles, and the median for a set of data. The length of the box represents the interquartile range. A vertical line inside the box represents the median. Horizontal lines (whiskers) represent the lower and upper fourths of the data. The bullets at each end are the **extreme values**.

Example Draw a box-and-whisker plot for the following data.
3, 7, 9, 14, 16, 19, 19, 25, 28

Step 1 Determine the quartiles and any outliers.

With the data ordered from least to greatest, determine the quartiles.

The median is 16. The lower quartile, Q_1, is $\frac{7 + 9}{2}$ or 8. The upper quartile, Q_3, is $\frac{19 + 25}{2}$ or 22.

The interquartile range is $22 - 8 = 14$.

Check to see if there are any **outliers**. An outlier is a data value that is at least 1.5 interquartile ranges less than Q_1 or greater than Q_3.

$8 - 1.5(14) = -13$ and $22 + 1.5(14) = 43$

There are no numbers less than -13 or greater than 43 in the data set. Therefore, there are no outliers.

Step 2 Draw and label a number line. Use a scale that includes the extreme values.

Step 3 Complete the box-and-whisker plot. Draw a box to designate the data between the upper and lower quartiles. Draw a line through the median. Draw a line from the lower quartile to the least value and from the upper quartile to the greatest value.

Exercises

Draw a box-and-whisker plot for each set of data.

1. 19, 49, 73, 30, 32, 46, 51, 30

2. 8, 2, 4, 2, 9, 13, 2, 5, 19, 24, 13, 1

3. 51, 55, 59, 20, 62, 48, 45, 44, 41, 71

4. 14.2, 15.3, 18.1, 16.5, 17.8, 17.5, 20.1, 15.8, 16.5, 17.9, 18.1, 19.0

Lesson 13-5

13-5 Study Guide and Intervention *(continued)*

Box-and-Whisker Plots

Parallel Box-and-Whisker Plots Two sets of data can be compared by drawing parallel box-and-whisker plots along the same number line.

Example The number of games won by the six Central Division baseball teams of the National League during the 2000 and the 1998 baseball seasons are shown in the table at the right. Draw a parallel box-and-whisker plot for the data and compare the data.

Team	2000	1998
St. Louis	95	83
Cincinnati	85	77
Milwaukee	73	74
Houston	72	102
Pittsburgh	69	69
Chicago	65	90

Step 1 With the data ordered from least to greatest, determine the quartiles for each year.

For 2000, the median is 72.5 games won. The lower quartile, Q_1, is 69. The upper quartile, Q_3, is 85. The interquartile range is $85 - 69 = 16$.

Check for outliers: $69 - 1.5(16) = 45$ and $85 + 1.5(16) = 109$.

There are no numbers less than 45 or greater than 109. Therefore, there are no outliers.

For 1998, the median is 80 games won. The lower quartile, Q_1, is 74. The upper quartile, Q_3, is 90. The interquartile range is 16.

Check for outliers: $74 - 1.5(16) = 50$ and $90 + 1.5(16) = 114$.

There are no numbers less than 50 or greater than 114. Therefore, there are no outliers.

Step 2 Draw the box-and-whisker plots along the same number line.

Step 3 Use the box-and-whisker plots to compare the data.

The range of games won is about the same for each year, but in general, the number of games won was higher in 1998. The median was also higher for 1998.

Exercises

Draw a parallel box-and-whisker plot for each pair of data. Compare the data.

1. A: 18, 41, 72, 45, 68, 75, 89, 34
B: 38, 39, 74, 56, 78, 68, 49, 78

2. A: 18, 34, 45, 34, 23, 32, 43, 14, 15
B: 19, 20, 40, 78, 56, 45, 35, 45, 91

14-1 Study Guide and Intervention

Counting Outcomes

Tree Diagrams One method used for counting the number of possible outcomes of an event is to draw a **tree diagram**. The last column of the tree diagram shows all of the possible outcomes. The list of all possible outcomes is called the **sample space**, and a specific outcome is called an **event**.

Lesson 14-1

Example 1 Suppose you can set up a stereo system with a choice of video, DVD, or laser disk players, a choice of cassette or graphic equalizer audio components, and a choice of single or dual speakers. Draw a tree diagram to show the sample space.

Player	Audio	Speaker	Outcomes
video	cassette	Single	VCS
		Dual	VCD
	graphic equalizer	Single	VGS
		Dual	VGD
DVD	cassette	Single	DCS
		Dual	DCD
	graphic equalizer	Single	DGS
		Dual	DGD
laser disk	cassette	Single	LCS
		Dual	LCD
	graphic equalizer	Single	LGS
		Dual	LGD

The tree diagram shows that there are 12 ways to set up the stereo system.

Example 2 A food stand offers ice cream cones in vanilla or chocolate flavors. It also offers fudge or caramel toppings, and it uses sugar or cake cones. Use a tree diagram to determine the number of possible ice cream cones.

Flavor	Toppings	Cone	Outcomes
vanilla	fudge	sugar	VFS
		cake	VFC
	caramel	sugar	VCS
		cake	VCC
chocolate	fudge	sugar	CFS
		cake	CFC
	caramel	sugar	CCS
		cake	CCC

The tree diagram shows that there are 8 possible ice cream cones.

Exercises

The spinner at the right is spun twice.

1. Draw a tree diagram to show the sample space.

2. How many outcomes are possible?

A pizza can be ordered with a choice of sausage, pepperoni, or mushrooms for toppings, a choice of thin or pan for the crust, and a choice of medium or large for the size.

3. Draw a tree diagram to show the sample space.

4. How many pizzas are possible?

14-1 **Study Guide and Intervention** *(continued)*

Counting Outcomes

The Fundamental Counting Principle Another way to count the number of possible outcomes is to use the Fundamental Counting Principle.

Fundamental Counting Principle	If an event M can occur in m ways and an event N can occur in n ways, then M followed by N can occur in $m \cdot n$ ways.

Example **Carly and Jake went to an arcade with 9 different games.**

a. In how many different orders can they play the games if they play each one only once?

The number of orders for playing can be found by multiplying the number of choices for each position. Let n represent the number of possible orders.

$n = 9 \cdot 8 \cdot 7 \cdot 6 \cdot 5 \cdot 4 \cdot 3 \cdot 2 \cdot 1 = 362{,}880$

There are 362,880 ways to play each of 9 arcade games once. This is also known as a **factorial**, or $n = 9! = 9 \cdot 8 \cdot 7 \cdot 6 \cdot 5 \cdot 4 \cdot 3 \cdot 2 \cdot 1$.

b. If they have only enough tokens to play 6 different games, how many ways can they do this?

Use the Fundamental Counting Principle to find the sample space. There are 9 choices for the first game, 8 choices for the second, and so on, down to 4 choices for the sixth game.

$n = 9 \cdot 8 \cdot 7 \cdot 6 \cdot 5 \cdot 4 = 60{,}480$

There are 60,480 ways to play 6 different arcade games once.

Exercises

Find the value of each expression.

1. 6!   **2.** 11!   **3.** 8!

4. A sub sandwich restaurant offers four types of sub sandwiches, three different types of potato chips, five types of bread, and six different beverages. How many different sandwich and drink combinations can you order?

5. How many outfits are possible if you can choose one from each of four shirts, three pairs of pants, two pairs of shoes, and two jackets?

6. In how many ways can you arrange 5 boxes of cereal on a shelf?

7. Seven students sit in a row in the auditorium. In how many ways can they arrange themselves?

8. Kinjal puts 12 different books on a shelf. In how many different ways can she arrange them?

14-2 Study Guide and Intervention

Permutations and Combinations

Permutations An arrangement or listing in which order or placement is important is called a **permutation**. For example the arrangement AB of choices A and B is different from the arrangement BA of these same two choices.

Permutations	$_nP_r = \dfrac{n!}{(n-r)!}$

Example 1 Find $_6P_2$.

$_nP_r = \dfrac{n!}{(n-r)!}$ Definition of $_nP_r$

$_6P_2 = \dfrac{6!}{(6-2)!}$ $n = 6, r = 2$

$= \dfrac{6!}{4!}$ Simplify.

$= \dfrac{6 \cdot 5 \cdot 4 \cdot 3 \cdot 2 \cdot 1}{4 \cdot 3 \cdot 2 \cdot 1}$ Definition of factorial

$= 6 \cdot 5$ or 30 Simplify.

There are 30 permutations of 6 objects taken 2 at a time.

Example 2 A specific program requires the user to enter a 5-digit password. The digits cannot repeat and can be any five of the digits 1, 2, 3, 4, 7, 8, and 9.

a. How many different passwords are possible?

$_nP_r = \dfrac{n!}{(n-r)!}$

$_7P_5 = \dfrac{7!}{(7-5)!}$

$= \dfrac{7 \cdot 6 \cdot 5 \cdot 4 \cdot 3 \cdot 2 \cdot 1}{2 \cdot 1}$

$= 7 \cdot 6 \cdot 5 \cdot 4 \cdot 3$ or 2520

There are 2520 ways to create a password.

b. What is the probability that the first two digits are odd numbers with the other digits any of the remaining numbers?

$P(\text{first two digits odd}) = \dfrac{\text{number of favorable outcomes}}{\text{number of possible outcomes}}$

Since there are 4 odd digits, the number of choices for the first digit is 4, and the number of choices for the second digit is 3. Then there are 5 choices left for the third digit, 4 for the fourth, and 3 for the fifth, so the number of favorable outcomes is $4 \cdot 3 \cdot 5 \cdot 4 \cdot 3$, or 720.

The probability is $\dfrac{720}{2520} \approx 28.6\%$.

Exercises

Evaluate of each expression.

1. $_7P_4$

2. $_{12}P_7$

3. $(_9P_9)(_{16}P_2)$

4. A club with ten members wants to choose a president, vice-president, secretary, and treasurer. Six of the members are women, and four are men.

    a. How many different sets of officers are possible?

    b. What is the probability that all officers will be women.

Lesson 14-2

14-2 Study Guide and Intervention (continued)

Permutations and Combinations

Combinations An arrangement or listing in which order is not important is called a **combination**. For example, AB and BA are the same combination of A and B.

Combinations	$_nC_r = \dfrac{n!}{(n-r)!r!}$

Example A club with ten members wants to choose a committee of four members. Six of the members are women, and four are men.

a. How many different committees are possible?

$$_nC_r = \frac{n!}{(n-r)!r!} \qquad \text{Definition of combination}$$

$$= \frac{10!}{(10-4)!4!} \qquad n = 10, r = 4$$

$$= \frac{10 \cdot 9 \cdot 8 \cdot 7}{4!} \qquad \text{Divide by the GCF 6!.}$$

$$= 210 \qquad \text{Simplify.}$$

There are 210 ways to choose a committee of four when order is not important.

b. If the committee is chosen randomly, what is the probability that two members of the committee are men?

There are $_4C_2 = \dfrac{4!}{(4-2)!2!} = 6$ ways to choose two men randomly, and there are

$_6C_2 = \dfrac{6!}{(6-4)!4!} = 15$ ways to choose two women randomly. By the Fundamental

Counting Principle, there are $6 \cdot 15$ or 90 ways to choose a committee with two men and two women.

$$\text{Probability (2 men and 2 women)} = \frac{\text{number of favorable outcomes}}{\text{number of possible outcomes}}$$

$$= \frac{90}{210} \text{ or about } 42.9\%$$

Exercises

Find the value of each expression.

1. $_7C_3$

2. $_{12}C_8$

3. $(_9C_9)(_{11}C_9)$

4. In how many ways can a club with 9 members choose a two-member sub-committee?

5. A book club offers its members a book each month for a year from a selection of 24 books. Ten of the books are biographies and 14 of the books are fiction.

  a. How many ways could the members select 12 books?

  b. What is the probability that 5 biographies and 7 fiction books will be chosen?

14-3 Study Guide and Intervention

Probability of Compound Events

Independent and Dependent Events
Compound events are made up of two or more simple events. The events can be **independent events** or they can be **dependent events**.

Probability of Independent Events	Outcome of first event does not affect outcome of second.	$P(A \text{ and } B) = P(A) \cdot P(B)$	Example: rolling a 6 on a die and then rolling a 5
Probability of Dependent Events	Outcome of first event does affect outcome of second.	$P(A \text{ and } B) = P(A) \cdot P(B \text{ following } A)$	Example: without replacing the first card, choosing an ace and then a king from a deck of cards

Example 1 Find the probability that you will roll a six and then a five when you roll a die twice.

By the definition of independent events, $P(A \text{ and } B) = P(A) \cdot P(B)$

First roll: $P(6) = \dfrac{1}{6}$

Second roll: $P(5) = \dfrac{1}{6}$

$P(6 \text{ and } 5) = P(6) \cdot P(5)$

$\qquad = \dfrac{1}{6} \cdot \dfrac{1}{6}$

$\qquad = \dfrac{1}{36}$

The probability that you will roll a six and then roll a five is $\dfrac{1}{36}$.

Example 2 A bag contains 3 red marbles, 2 green marbles, and 4 blue marbles. Two marbles are drawn randomly from the bag and not replaced. Find the probability that both marbles are blue.

By the definition of dependent events, $P(A \text{ and } B) = P(A) \cdot P(B \text{ following } A)$

First marble: $P(\text{blue}) = \dfrac{4}{9}$

Second marble: $P(\text{blue}) = \dfrac{3}{8}$

$P(\text{blue, blue}) = \dfrac{4}{9} \cdot \dfrac{3}{8}$

$\qquad = \dfrac{12}{72}$

$\qquad = \dfrac{1}{6}$

The probability of drawing two blue marbles is $\dfrac{1}{6}$.

Exercises

A bag contains 3 red, 4 blue, and 6 yellow marbles. One marble is selected at a time, and once a marble is selected, it is not replaced. Find each probability.

1. $P(\text{2 yellow})$

2. $P(\text{red, yellow})$

3. $P(\text{blue, red, yellow})$

4. George has two red socks and two white socks in a drawer. What is the probability of picking a red sock and a white sock in that order if the first sock is not replaced?

5. Phyllis drops a penny in a pond, and then she drops a nickel in the pond. What is the probability that both coins land with tails showing?

6. A die is rolled and a penny is dropped. Find the probability of rolling a two and showing a tail.

14-3 Study Guide and Intervention (continued)

Probability of Compound Events

Mutually Exclusive and Inclusive Events Events that cannot occur at the same time are called **mutually exclusive**. If two events are not mutually exclusive, they are called **inclusive**.

Probability of Mutually Exclusive Events	$P(A \text{ or } B) = P(A) + P(B)$	$P(\text{rolling a 2 or a 3 on a die}) = P(2) + P(3) = \frac{1}{3}$
Probability of Inclusive Events	$P(A \text{ or } B) =$ $P(A) + P(B) - P(A \text{ and } B)$	$P(\text{King or Heart}) = P(K) + P(H) - P(K \text{ and } H) = \frac{9}{26}$

Example Suppose a card is drawn from a standard deck of 52 cards. Find the probability of drawing a king or a queen.

Drawing a king or a queen are mutually exclusive events.
By the definition of mutually exclusive events, $P(A \text{ or } B) = P(A) + P(B)$.

$P(A) = P(\text{king}) = \frac{4}{52} = \frac{1}{13}$ $P(B) = P(\text{queen}) = \frac{4}{52} = \frac{1}{13}$

$P(\text{king or queen}) = \frac{1}{13} + \frac{1}{13}$

$= \frac{2}{13}$

The probability of drawing a king or a queen is $\frac{2}{13}$.

Exercises

A bag contains 2 red, 5 blue, and 7 yellow marbles. Find each probability.

1. $P(\text{yellow or red})$ 2. $P(\text{red or not yellow})$ 3. $P(\text{blue or red or yellow})$

One card is drawn from a standard deck of 52 cards. Find each probability.

4. $P(\text{jack or red})$ 5. $P(\text{red or black})$

6. $P(\text{jack or clubs})$ 7. $P(\text{queen or less than 3})$

8. $P(5 \text{ or } 6)$ 9. $P(\text{diamond or spade})$

10. In a math class, 12 out of 15 girls are 14 years old and 14 out of 17 boys are 14 years old. What is the probability of selecting a girl or a 14-year old from this class?

14-4 Study Guide and Intervention
Probability Distributions

Random Variables and Probability Distributions A random variable X is a variable whose value is the numerical outcome of a random event.

Example A teacher asked her students how many siblings they have. The results are shown in the table at the right.

Number of Siblings	Number of Students
0	1
1	15
2	8
3	2
4	1

a. Find the probability that a randomly selected student has 2 siblings.

The random variable X can equal 0, 1, 2, 3, or 4. In the table, the value $X = 2$ is paired with 8 outcomes, and there are 27 students surveyed.

$$P(X = 2) = \frac{2 \text{ siblings}}{27 \text{ students surveyed}}$$

$$= \frac{8}{27}$$

The probability that a randomly selected student has 2 siblings is $\frac{8}{27}$, or 29.6%.

b. Find the probability that a randomly selected student has at least three siblings.

$$P(X \geq 3) = \frac{2 + 1}{27}$$

The probability that a randomly selected student has at least 3 siblings is $\frac{1}{9}$, or 11.1%.

Exercises

For Exercises 1–3, use the grade distribution shown at the right. A grade of A = 5, B = 4, C = 3, D = 2, F = 1.

X = Grade	5	4	3	2	1
Number of Students	6	9	5	4	1

1. Find the probability that a randomly selected student in this class received a grade of C.

2. Find the probability that a randomly selected student in this class received a grade lower than a C.

3. What is the probability that a randomly selected student in this class passes the course, that is, gets at least a D?

4. The table shows the results of tossing 3 coins 50 times. What is the probability of getting 2 or 3 heads?

X = Number of Heads	0	1	2	3
Number of Times	6	20	19	5

Lesson 14-4

14-4 Study Guide and Intervention *(continued)*

Probability Distributions

Probability Distributions The probabilities associated with every possible value of the random variable X make up what are called the **probability distribution** for that variable. A probability distribution has the following properties.

Properties of a Probability Distribution	1. The probability of each value of X is greater than or equal to 0.
	2. The probabilities for all values of X add up to 1.

The probability distribution for a random variable can be given in a table or in a **probability histogram** and used to obtain other information.

Example The data from the example on page 849 can be used to determine a probability distribution and to make a probability histogram.

X = Number of Siblings	$P(X)$
0	0.037
1	0.556
2	0.296
3	0.074
4	0.037

Probability Histogram

a. Show that the probability distribution is valid.

For each value of X, the probability is greater than or equal to 0 and less than or equal to 1. Also, the sum of the probabilities is 1.

b. What is the probability that a student chosen at random has fewer than 2 siblings?

Because the events are independent, the probability of fewer than 2 siblings is the sum of the probability of 0 siblings and the probability of 1 sibling, or $0.037 + 0.556 = 0.593$.

Exercises

The table at the right shows the probability distribution for students by school enrollment in the United States in 1997. Use the table for Exercises 1–3.

X = Type of School	$P(X)$
Elementary = 1	0.562
Secondary = 2	0.219
Higher Education = 3	0.219

Source: *The New York Times Almanac*

1. Show that the probability distribution is valid.

2. If a student is chosen at random, what is the probability that the student is in elementary or secondary school?

3. Make a probability histogram of the data.

Probability Histogram

14-5 Study Guide and Intervention

Probability Simulations

Theoretical and Experimental Probability

The probability used to describe events mathematically is called **theoretical probability**. For example, the mathematical probability of rolling a 4 with a number cube is $\frac{1}{6}$, or $P(4) = \frac{1}{6}$. **Experimental probability** is the ratio of the number of times an outcome occurs in an experiment to the total number of events or trials, known as the **relative frequency**.

Experimental probability	$\dfrac{\text{frequency of an outcome}}{\text{total number of trials}}$

Example 1 Matt recorded that it rained 8 times in November and snowed 3 times. The other days, it was sunny. There are 30 days in November. Suppose Matt uses these results to predict November's weather next year. What is the probability that a day in November will be sunny?

$$\text{Experimental Probability} = \frac{\text{frequency of outcome}}{\text{total number of trials}}$$
$$= \frac{(30 - 8 - 3)}{30}$$
$$= \frac{19}{30} = 63.3\%$$

The probability that it will be sunny on a day in November is 63.3%.

Example 2 A football team noticed that 9 of the last 20 coin tosses to choose which team would receive the ball first resulted in tails. What is the experimental probability of the coin landing on tails? What is the theoretical probability?

$$\text{Experimental Probability} = \frac{\text{frequency of outcome}}{\text{total number of trials}}$$
$$= \frac{\text{number of tails}}{\text{total number of tosses}}$$
$$= \frac{9}{20} = 45\%$$

In this case, the experimental probability that a coin toss will be tails is 45%. If the coin is fair, the mathematical probability is 50%.

Exercises

A math class decided to test whether a die is fair, that is, whether the experimental probability equals the theoretical probability. The results for 100 rolls are shown at the right. Use the information for Exercises 1–3.

1: 1	2: 15
3: 4	4: 13
5: 15	6: 42

1. What is the theoretical probability of rolling a 6?

2. What is the experimental probability of rolling a 6?

3. Is the die fair? Explain your reasoning.

Lesson 14-5

14-5 Study Guide and Intervention *(continued)*

Probability Simulations

Performing Simulations A method that is often used to find experimental probability is a **simulation**. A simulation allows you to use objects to act out an event that would be difficult or impractical to perform.

> **Example** In one baseball season, Pete was able to get a base hit 42 of the 254 times he was at bat.

a. What could be used to simulate his getting a base hit?

First find the experimental probability.

Experimental Probability = $\frac{\text{frequency of outcome}}{\text{total number of trials}}$

$= \frac{42}{254}$ or 16.5%

Notice that the experimental probability is about $\frac{1}{6}$. Therefore use a spinner like the one at the right with 6 equally likely outcomes.

b. Describe a way to simulate his next 10 times at bat.

Let an outcome of 1 correspond to Pete's getting a base hit. Let all other outcomes correspond to his *not* getting a hit. Spin the spinner once to simulate a time at bat. Record the result and repeat this 9 more times.

> **Exercises**

1. What could you use to simulate the outcome of guessing on a 20 question true-false test?

2. What could you use to simulate the outcome of guessing on a 20-question multiple choice test with 4 alternative answers labeled A, B, C, and D for each question?

For Exercises 3–4, use the following information.

Main Street Supermarket randomly gives each shopper a free two-liter bottle of cola during the Saturday shopping hours. The supermarket sells 6 different types of cola.

3. What could be used to perform a simulation of this situation?

4. How could you use this simulation to model the next 50 bottles of cola given out.

5. At a picnic, there were 2 peanut butter sandwiches, 2 chicken sandwiches, a tuna sandwich, and a turkey sandwich in a cooler. Describe a simulation that could be used to find the probability of randomly picking a certain sandwich from the cooler.